Optimal Adaptive
Control Systems

MATHEMATICS IN SCIENCE AND ENGINEERING

A SERIES OF MONOGRAPHS AND TEXTBOOKS

Edited by Richard Bellman

University of Southern California

1. Tracy Y. Thomas. Concepts from Tensor Analysis and Differential Geometry. Second Edition. 1965
2. Tracy Y. Thomas. Plastic Flow and Fracture in Solids. 1961
3. Rutherford Aris. The Optimal Design of Chemical Reactors: A Study in Dynamic Programming. 1961
4. Joseph LaSalle and Solomon Lefschetz. Stability by Liapunov's Direct Method with Applications. 1961
5. George Leitmann (ed.). Optimization Techniques: With Applications to Aerospace Systems. 1962
6. Richard Bellman and Kenneth L. Cooke. Differential-Difference Equations. 1963
7. Frank A. Haight. Mathematical Theories of Traffic Flow. 1963
8. F. V. Atkinson. Discrete and Continuous Boundary Problems. 1964
9. A. Jeffrey and T. Taniuti. Non-Linear Wave Propagation: With Applications to Physics and Magnetohydrodynamics. 1964
10. Julius T. Tou. Optimum Design of Digital Control Systems. 1963
11. Harley Flanders. Differential Forms: With Applications to the Physical Sciences. 1963
12. Sanford M. Roberts. Dynamic Programming in Chemical Engineering and Process Control. 1964
13. Solomon Lefschetz. Stability of Nonlinear Control Systems. 1965
14. Dimitris N. Chorafas. Systems and Simulation. 1965
15. A. A. Pervozvanskii. Random Processes in Nonlinear Control Systems. 1965
16. Marshall C. Pease, III. Methods of Matrix Algebra. 1965
17. V. E. Beneš. Mathematical Theory of Connecting Networks and Telephone Traffic. 1965
18. William F. Ames. Nonlinear Partial Differential Equations in Engineering. 1965

MATHEMATICS IN SCIENCE AND ENGINEERING

19. J. Aczél. Lectures on Functional Equations and Their Applications. 1966

20. R. E. Murphy. Adaptive Processes in Economic Systems. 1965

21. S. E. Dreyfus. Dynamic Programming and the Calculus of Variations. 1965

22. A. A. Fel'dbaum. Optimal Control Systems. 1965

23. A. Halanay. Differential Equations: Stability, Oscillations, Time Lags. 1966

24. Namik Oğuztöreli. Time Lag Control Systems. 1966

25. David Sworder. Optimal Adaptive Control Systems.

In preparation

Milton Ash. Optimal Shutdown Control of Nuclear Reactors. 1966

Dimitris N. Chorafas. Control Systems Functions and Programming Approaches. In Two Volumes

A. Kaufmann. Graphs, Dynamic Programming, and Finite Games

Solomon Marcus. Algebraic Linguistics; Analytical Models

Minoru Urabe. Nonlinear Autonomous Oscillations

A. Kaufmann and R. Cruon. Dynamic Programming: Sequential Scientific Management

N. P. Erugin. Linear Systems of Ordinary Differential Equations

George Leitmann (ed.). Optimization: A Variational Approach

A .M. Liapunov. Stability of Motion

Optimal Adaptive Control Systems

David Sworder

DEPARTMENT OF ELECTRICAL ENGINEERING
UNIVERSITY OF SOUTHERN CALIFORNIA
LOS ANGELES, CALIFORNIA

1966

Academic Press New York and London

ACADEMIC PRESS INC.
111 Fifth Avenue, New York, New York 10003

United Kingdom Edition published by
ACADEMIC PRESS INC. (LONDON) LTD.
Berkeley Square House, London W.1

LIBRARY OF CONGRESS CATALOG CARD NUMBER: 65-26411

PRINTED IN THE UNITED STATES OF AMERICA

Preface

In application of feedback control theory, an engineer frequently is faced with the problem of designing a compensation device for a plant whose characteristics are not known precisely. This situation may be occasioned by the nonzero tolerances implicit in various specifications of the system to be controlled, or perhaps by uncertainty with respect to the environmental conditions in which the system operates. This difficulty is offset, at least in part, by one of the basic properties of feedback: a reduction in the sensitivity of response of the closed-loop system to variations in the open-loop characteristics. If an engineer can determine a nominal mathematical model for the process he endeavors to control, and if the predicted variations from this model are small, he is certainly justified in selecting the control element through an analysis of the behavior of the model. Such a procedure implies that the character of the actual process will not change so radically as to cause unacceptable system performance.

In many situations, however, such a premise is not justified. For example, the controlled system may be subject to such varied environmental conditions that a controller that is not actively altered as the external disturbances change cannot produce adequate behavior. Consequently engineers have sought compensation devices which adapt to the changes in the system attributes in the sense that the control rule is modified in response to changes in the system response. In this book the optimal control of processes with incomplete mathematical descriptions is analyzed. Particular attention is given to the properties of this class of control problems which distinguish it from the typical optimal control problem in which the description of the process to be controlled is specified.

The material in this exposition can be divided into three main parts. In Chapters 1–3 the control problem is formulated in detail and the theory of statistical decisions is employed to provide a framework for the solution. In Chapter 4 a recurrence formula is derived which must be satisfied by an important class of optimal control policies. In Chapters 5 and 6 several comprehensive examples are analyzed. They not only serve to illustrate the synthesis techniques of Chapter 4, but also aid in clarifying some of the ambiguity related to the meaning *optimization* and *identification* in adaptive control systems.

This book is intended for an engineering audience and therefore the game-theoretic material necessary for the final chapters is developed in some detail in the first part. It is assumed that the reader is familiar with the use of the state space description of dynamical systems and also with such elementary statistical notions as the expectation and variance of a random variable.

I wish to express my thanks to Professor C. T. Leondes for his useful advice. This research was supported by grants AFOSR-699-65, under the direction of Professor Leondes while I was attending the University of California at Los Angeles. I also thank Professors M. Aoki and T. Ferguson for their comments on this work.

Los Angeles, California
March 1966

DAVID D. SWORDER

Contents

CHAPTER 4

Synthesis of Bayes Control Policies for Discrete Time Adaptive Control Systems

CHAPTER 5

Control of Linear Systems with a Markov Property

CHAPTER 6

Suboptimal Adaptive Control Systems

CHAPTER 1

Introduction to the Theory of Optimal Adaptive Control Systems

1. Basic Structure of Optimal Control Processes

Before we specify what is meant by the phrase "optimal adaptive control system," let us examine the fundamental properties of an optimal control system. As a starting point for any practical procedure for synthesizing a compensation network in a control loop, the designer is given a fixed object and is told the function which the object is supposed to perform. The object to be controlled, often referred to as the plant, is called fixed because its properties are usually determined by considerations other than ease of control. For example, one might be given the mechanical characteristics of an inertial platform and the electromechanical characteristics of the gyros to be used to sense platform motion. The task of the control system designer might be to build a device which will generate platform torquing signals that cause the orientation of the gimbal structure to be maintained in such a way that the gyro pickoff signals are identically zero.

Let the plant transfer operator be denoted by f and consider the situation presented in Fig. 1.1. The engineer must design a compensation device which will generate an input function, $v(t)$, that will cause the plant output, $x(t)$, to respond in the desired manner. Both $v(t)$ and $x(t)$ will, in general, be vector quantities.

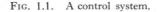

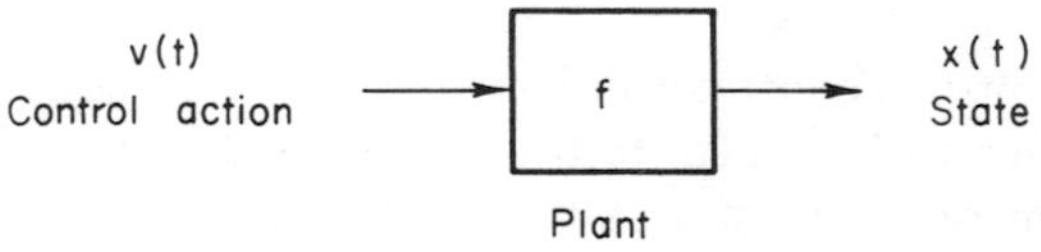

FIG. 1.1. A control system.

Before this problem can be solved, some structure must be added to these basic ideas. On the one hand, the desired system performance may not be attainable. In the example mentioned previously it is not possible to maintain the gyro pickoff signals identically zero under normal operating conditions with the available components and energy sources. In this case the failure to meet the performance specification is the result of the undue strictness with which it limits the acceptable response. In applications the engineer may view the desired output as a nominal value for the system response and he may then select a compensation element from those permissible in the particular situation in such a way as to "minimize" the difference between the actual response of the plant and the specified response.

Obviously, the deviation which exists between the actual and ideal system behavior cannot always be minimized because it will frequently be a function of time or perhaps even a stochastic process. One way to avoid this obstacle is to provide a performance functional which associates a real number with the discrepancy in the system response. To formulate this functional in such a way that it retains the essential nature of the system specifications may be quite a difficult task. This is especially true when there are compromises between requirements of a basically different nature; i.e., size, weight, cost, and performance. For the purposes of this exposition it will be assumed that this difficulty has been overcome, and the there exists a real valued function of the system performance which measures the effectiveness of the control. Furthermore, we will assume that the control rule is better if this index number is smaller. Thus, the basic optimal control problem is formulated in the following way. The control system designer is given a description of the behavior of the fixed element, f, and a criterion of performance. He then explores the set of control policies which are allowed in this system and selects one which minimizes the performance measure. Of course, there may be problems related to the existence of such a control policy, but under conditions usually met in practice an optimal rule will exist.

Although optimal control problems have this fundamental structure, they may differ with respect to the particular features of such things as the amount of information available to the compensation element. For example, if the engineer wishes to cause the plant output to follow a command input, $\tilde{x}(t)$, then he might permit the control action to depend explicitly on some measured function of $\tilde{x}(t)$, say $h[\tilde{x}(t)]$; that is,

$$v = \bar{v}[t, h(\tilde{x}(t))],$$

where $\bar{v}$ is a function over an appropriate domain which takes on values within the set of allowable control actions. According to our desire to have $x(t)$ traverse a designated trajectory, or follow some randomly varying quantity, $\tilde{x}(t)$ may be deterministic or random.

A particular example of this class of problems that has received much attention in the literature of control theory is the time optimal problem. Here, $\tilde{x}(t) \equiv 0$ and the initial state, $x(0)$, is fixed. Since the input is identically zero, the control policy becomes a function only of time. The engineer must select that time function from those allowable in such a way that the system state is transferred from $x(0)$ to the state $x(t) = 0$ in minimum time.

If, as in the previous example, no information on $x(t)$ is available to the compensation during the control process, the system is called open loop. This configuration will yield adequate performance if the complete characterization of f is known when the control policy is initiated. It becomes less satisfactory if there are certain random or unknown elements in the plant or in the environment where the plant operates. For example, a constant offset of unknown value may be added to $v(t)$ in the channel transmitting the control action to the plant. The actual output may now be quite different from what would be predicted in the absence of offset. It is clear that such disturbances can produce totally intolerable system behavior. Consequently, the additional system complexity necessary to obtain continuous state measurements is often justified. Thus, some measured function of the plant output, $g(x(t))$, might be fed back to the controller. A feedback control rule of the form

$$v = \bar{v}(t, h(\tilde{x}(t)), g(x(t)))$$

could then be employed.

Before we proceed further, let us employ these ideas in considering a very simple single-stage process. In particular, notice the essential dependence of the control action on the type of information available to the controller. The plant is described by the scalar difference equation

$$x_1 = ax_0 + \xi v_0 , \qquad \xi \neq 0:$$

Let an input, $\tilde{x}_1$, and a criterion of performance, $h(\cdot)$, be given:

$$h(\tilde{x}_1, x) = (\tilde{x}_1 - x_1)^2.$$

The engineer must design a controller which will generate the control action v_0 in such a way that $h(\tilde{x}_1, x)$ is minimized. Let $\mathrm{Nor}(\theta, \sigma^2)$ denote a normal probability distribution function with mean θ and variance σ^2. Let us suppose that the control system designer knows that the probability distribution function for x_0 is $\mathrm{Nor}(\theta_x, \sigma_x^2)$ and that the probability distribution function for $\tilde{x}_1$ is $\mathrm{Nor}(\theta_{\tilde{x}}, \sigma_{\tilde{x}}^2)$. We assume $\tilde{x}_1$ and x_0 to be statistically independent.

The criterion of performance can be written in such a way that it is explicitly a function of the control action v_0:

$$h(\tilde{x}_1, x) = \xi^2 \left(\frac{\tilde{x}_1 - ax_0}{\xi} - v_0\right)^2.$$

It is apparent that the control problem can be reformulated as a problem of estimating the random variable $(\tilde{x}_1 - ax_0) \mid \xi$ with a quadratic weighting of error.

Let us now examine the solution to this design problem under various restrictions on the data available to the control element. The simplest case is that which permits the compensation to use measurements of both $\tilde{x}_1$ and x_0. If the optimal control action is denoted by $(v_0)_{\min}$, then

$$(v_0)_{\min} = \frac{\tilde{x}_1 - ax_0}{\xi}$$

and

$$\inf_{v_0} h(\tilde{x}_1, x) = 0.$$

If $\tilde{x}_1$ can be measured or is known *a priori* but x_0 is unknown, then $h(\tilde{x}_1, x)$ is a random variable. Consequently, $h(\tilde{x}_1, x)$ cannot be used directly as a performance index because it does not associate a real number with each control action. This dilemma is frequently resolved by using $E\{h(\tilde{x}_1, x)\}$ as the criterion functional. $E\{\ \}$ is the symbol which will be used to denote the operation of statistical expectation. If we wish to form this average with respect to only one variable, say x_1, of a function of several variables we will denote this by $E_{x_1}\{f(x_1, x_2, \ldots, x_n)\}$. This average can also be written as a conditional expectation; i.e., $E\{f(x_1, x_2, ..., x_n) \mid x_2, x_3, ..., x_n\}$. In the system under investigation the criterion of performance is $E\{h(\tilde{x}_1, x) \mid a, \xi, \tilde{x}_1\}$. It can be shown that the best estimate of a real parameter with a quadratic loss is the *a posteriori* mean of the distribution for the parameter. Accordingly,

$$(v_0)_{\min} = E\left\{\frac{\tilde{x}_1 - ax_0}{\xi} \,\middle|\, a, \xi, \tilde{x}_1\right\} = \frac{\tilde{x}_1 - a\theta_x}{\xi}.$$

In this example the *a posteriori* mean of x_0 is equal to the *a priori* mean, θ_x. Using the above control policy, the expected cost of the process becomes

$$\inf_{v_0} E\{h(\tilde{x}_1, x)| \, a, \xi, \tilde{x}_1\} = \xi^2 E\left\{\left(\frac{ax_0}{\xi} - \frac{a\theta_x}{\xi}\right)^2\right\} = a^2\sigma_x^{\,2}.$$

We can show in the same manner that if x_0 can be measured and $\tilde{x}_1$ cannot, then

$$(v_0)_{\min} = \frac{\theta_{\tilde{x}} - ax_0}{\xi}$$

and

$$\inf_{v_0} E\{h(\tilde{x}_1, x)| \, a, \xi, x_0\} = \sigma_{\tilde{x}}^2.$$

Finally, if neither $\tilde{x}_1$ nor x_0 can be measured,

$$(v_0)_{\min} = \frac{\theta_{\tilde{x}} - a\theta_x}{\xi}$$

and

$$\inf_{v_0} E\{h(\tilde{x}_1, x)| \, a, \xi\} = \sigma_{\tilde{x}}^2 + a^2\sigma_x^{\,2}.$$

The above example illustrates the essential characteristics of the optimal control problem. The engineer is given the equations which describe the fixed object in the loop; a set of allowable controls; and a set of observable data on the past and present states of the input and the plant, and on the past history of the control action. On the basis of this information, a control action is generated in such a way as to minimize the value of an appropriate index of performance. Both the object to be controlled and the observation mechanism may be contaminated with some type of random disturbance, but it is presumed that the statistical characterization of these disturbances is known to the control system designer.

2. Introduction to Adaptive Control Theory

The essential property which distinguishes optimal control problems is that the control system designer has, in principle, sufficient information available to design a compensation element which will result in a minimum of the performance measure. One technique of discovering the optimal control is as follows. To each control rule, $\bar{u}$, in the set of allowable control rules, Γ, we assign a real number $H(\bar{u})$ which is the cost of the control process using the policy $\bar{u}$. The engineer now inspects this set of numbers, and if there exists a $\bar{u}_0 \in \Gamma$ such that

$$H(\bar{u}_0) = \inf_{\bar{u} \in \Gamma} H(\bar{u}),$$

then we say that $\bar{u}_0$ is an optimal control policy for the system. Since there may be many control rules with the same cost, there may be many optimal control rules. The underlying feature of this problem which permitted a solution to be obtained was that if $\bar{v} \in \Gamma$ and if $\bar{\omega} \in \Gamma$, then either

$$H(\bar{v}) < H(\bar{\omega})$$

or

$$H(\bar{v}) = H(\bar{\omega})$$

or

$$H(\bar{v}) > H(\bar{\omega}).$$

Thus, H induces a total ordering on the set of allowable controls.

The functional H creates a total ordering on Γ because a complete characterization is provided for all other elements of the control system; that is, the plant equations are given to the control system designer, and the statistical description of the random disturbances are sufficiently complete to account for their influence on the performance index. The question now arises as to the effect on the problem formulation of a system description in which certain elements are not known. For example, it might be supposed that a parameter in the description of the object to be controlled or the observation mechanism is unknown. In this case the controller must accomplish some type of learning operation which will yield information about the unknown system parameter in order to provide an adequate control policy as measured by the performance criterion. The adjective "adaptive" will be attached to such systems. It should be noted that various definitions for "adaptive control" have appeared in the literature on control theory. In this book "adaptive" will emphasize an uncertainty in the process description.

To motivate the definitions and results which follow it is well to consider with the aid of a very simple example how the adaptive problems differ from those described in the first section. More comprehensive examples will be provided in the sequel after a more rigorous treatment of the problem is presented. Again we will analyze a single-stage process in which the fixed element of the loop is described by the scalar difference equation

$$x_1 = ax_0 + \xi v_0 , \qquad x_0 = x(0).$$

The performance index will be given by

$$h(x, \tilde{x}, v) = (x_1)^2.$$

As we have seen, if a, ξ, and x_0 were known, this optimal control problem would admit of the simple solution

$$(\bar{v}_0)_{\min} = -\frac{ax_0}{\xi} .$$

Suppose, however, that nothing is known about ξ except that

$$\xi \in S = \{\xi \mid -1 \leqslant \xi \leqslant 1\}.$$

For any real number v_0 the criterion functional can be written as

$$H(v_0) = (ax_0 + \xi v_0)^2. \tag{1.1}$$

It is evident that the performance index is a function of the unknown system parameter and it does not induce a total ordering on the set of allowable controls. Instead, the ordering generated by $h(x, \tilde{x}, v)$ is a partial ordering and it is not obvious that a "best" control rule exists in this circumstance.

Each element of the set $K = \{v_0 \mid v_0 \leqslant -\mid ax_0 \mid \text{ or } v_0 \geqslant \mid ax_0 \mid\}$ possesses a rather interesting peculiarity. There exists a value of $\xi \in S$ such that $H(v_0) = 0$. It is clear that if $v \in K$, there does not exist any $u \neq v$ such that $H(u) \leqslant H(v)$ for all $\xi \in S$. This weak optimality property will later be generalized by introducing the concept of admissibility.

The ordering induced by the criterion of performance leads

the engineer to a set of control policies, each possessing a rather mild optimality property, rather than a single optimal control rule which is needed for a control application. To provide the required total ordering of the control policies, two possible approaches appear reasonable. If there exists some *a priori* knowledge about the relative probabilities of the various elements of S, then we might view ξ as a random variable with known probability distribution function and employ the expected value of the criterion functional as the performance measure. Such a procedure is frequently referred to as a Bayes principle of choice. In the foregoing example let the *a priori* probability density of the elements of S be

$$p(\xi) = \frac{-k\xi + 1}{2} I_{[-1,1]}, \qquad -1 \leqslant k \leqslant 1.$$

$I_{[-1,1]}$ is the characteristic function of the interval $[-1, 1]$. Then, the expected value of $H(v)$ with respect to this probability density function becomes

$$\begin{aligned} H(v) &= E\{(ax_0 + \xi v_0)^2 \mid a, x_0, v_0\} \\ &= (ax_0)^2 - \tfrac{2}{3} a x_0 v_0 k + \frac{2}{3}\frac{(v_0)^2}{2}. \end{aligned}$$

Clearly, this expression is minimized by selecting

$$(v_0)_{\min} = a x_0 k,$$

and we obtain the following value for H:

$$H((v_0)_{\min}) = (ax_0)^2(1 - \tfrac{1}{3}k^2).$$

Observe that if $k = 0$, then $(v_0)_{\min} = 0$. The control policy which generates a zero output for all initial conditions, x_0, is not only a Bayes control policy with respect to $p(\xi) = \frac{1}{2} I_{[1,1]}$, but also from Eq. (1.1) it is evident that $H(0) = (ax_0)^2$. For this control rule the effectiveness of the control is independent of $\xi \in S$. Such a controller is called an equalizer policy.

If it is not possible to make an *a priori* probability statement about the unspecified parameters, a Bayes policy does not seem to possess the features which are desired in an optimal control. Some *a priori* distribution could simply be postulated and the Bayes policy evaluated for the assumed distribution, but such a procedure is rather arbitrary.

Without any prior statistical knowledge a "worst case" attitude might seem appropriate, and a control would be sought which minimizes the maximum value of the criterion functional. In this example a total ordering on the set of allowable controls would be induced by $\sup_{\xi \in S} H(v)$. Such an ordering suffers from the practical drawback that the $\sup_{\xi \in S}$ operation can be quite difficult to apply. This is particularly true if the domain of this operator is extended and the set of all probability distributions over S is considered to be the appropriate domain. This constitutes such a large class of elements that direct methods of finding the minimax control policy are usually not satisfactory. In this event the role of equalizer control rules is quite important. It will later be shown that $v_0 = 0$ is the minimax control action in our example.

3. Introduction to Zero-Sum Two-Person Games

Since much of what follows in this book will be intimately connected with the theory of games and statistical decisions, it would be well to provide a cursory introduction to some of the fundamental ideas of game theory. Consider the following game between an entity which we will call nature or player 1, and the engineer referred to as player 2. Players 1 and 2 simultaneously select a number from the doublet $\{1, 2\}$. These numbers are compared and if both players have chosen the same number player 1 pays to player 2 the sum in dollars of the selections of the two players. If, however, the players have chosen different numbers, player 2 pays to player 1 the sum in dollars of the selections made.

If we denote by j the strategy of choosing the number j, then each player has the choice of two strategies, 1 and 2. The possible outcomes of the game can be presented in the form of a table in which the loss to the engineer is displayed for all allowable strategies.

		engineer v: 1	2
nature θ	1	-2	3
	2	3	-4

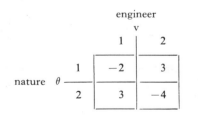

There are three fundamental elements which characterize a zero-sum two-person game. They are

(1) a nonempty set, Θ, of possible strategies for nature,

(2) a nonempty set, V, of possible strategies for the engineer, and

(3) a scalar cost function, H, defined on $V \times \Theta$.

In the single-stage game considered here

$$\Theta = V = \{1, 2\},$$

and H is defined by the table of outcomes. Since a game is completely described by these three elements, it is considered equivalent to the triplet (Θ, V, H) in which Θ and V are nonempty sets and H is a scalar valued function on $V \times \Theta$.

In the game which we have proposed, it is not clear what a good strategy for the engineer would be since he may lose money with either element of V. Consider, therefore, the following variation of the original game. Players 1 and 2 again select their numbers simultaneously, but now player 1 must notify player 2 in advance what his strategy will be. This is certainly an advantageous situation for the engineer because he can now assure himself of a financial gain for any strategy nature selects. To avoid the certain loss of money which occurs in this modified game, nature might seek to enlarge her class of allowable strategies. One method of doing this would be to designate two nonnegative scalars p and q such that $p + q = 1$. Then a randomized strategy for nature would be to choose the number 1 with probability p and the number 2 with probability q. If we denote the set of all probability distributions over Θ by Θ^*, then a randomized strategy for nature is a selection of an element $\theta_0^* \in \Theta^*$. Observe that if nature must inform the engineer of her strategy before the engineer decides upon a strategy, it is expedient for her to make the choice from Θ^* since the expected gain for nature may in this way be significantly increased.

Clearly, if the positions of the players are reversed, it will be advisable for the engineer to employ a randomized strategy to avoid a certain loss of money to nature. Hence, if randomized strategies are permitted the game is described by the triplet (Θ^*, V^*, H) where H is now defined over $V^* \times \Theta^*$ and represents the engineer's expected loss.

It is evident from this examination that the strategy utilized by the engineer will be determined in part by the amount of data available to him. For example, if no information on the strategy of nature is obtainable by the engineer, there is no uniformly best strategy for him. If, on the other hand, nature discloses that it will use the strategy $\theta_0^* \in \Theta^*$, then the engineer would choose that element of V^* which causes a minimum of H. The dependence of good strategies in a two-person game on information gathered about the opponents strategy is very basic and leads to the idea of a statistical game with a single experiment.

Utilizing an experiment allows the engineer to "spy" on nature and gather information on the strategy which is being used against him. In statistical games it does not seem plausible to attribute to nature the character of a conscious opponent and we, therefore, do not usually grant to player 1 the opportunity to observe the strategy of player 2. Let us assume that the engineer performs an experiment with an outcome z. In general, z will be a random variable with probability distribution function $P(z \mid \theta)$. On the basis of the observed value of z the engineer will choose a strategy in V.

Returning to the earlier example, imagine the following game. Nature chooses an element θ of Θ as its strategy. The engineer then performs an experiment with outcome z which is described by the probability mass function

$$\text{Prob}(z \mid \theta) = 1 \qquad \text{if} \quad z = \theta,$$

$$\text{Prob}(z \mid \theta) = 0 \qquad \text{if} \quad z \neq \theta.$$

From this experiment the engineer learns the true value of θ for the game and can act accordingly.

Let the range of z be Z. Then a nonrandomized or pure strategy for the engineer in a statistical game is a function from Z to V; that is, to each outcome of the experiment the engineer assigns a strategy from V. A (measurable) function which maps Z into V is called a decision function and the set of all such functions, Γ, is the set of pure strategies for the engineer. Note the lack of symmetry in the rules which govern the play of nature and the engineer in the statistical game. This anomaly is occasioned by the lack of deliberate effort on the part of nature to increase the engineer's loss.

If all the necessary averages are assumed to exist, the risk, ρ, of a particular decision function, d, is defined as

$$\rho(\theta, d) = \int H(\theta, d(z))\, dP(z \mid \theta),$$

where ρ is a function on $\Theta \times \Gamma$ which yields the expected cost of the process for pure strategies on the part of both nature and the engineer. A statistical game with a single experiment can, thus, be described by the triple (Θ, Γ, ρ). Generalizing this game to include randomized strategies for both nature and the engineer can be accomplished in a straightforward manner. The mixed extension of a statistical game is described by the triple $(\Theta^*, \Gamma^*, \rho)$.

As an example of a statistical game with a single experiment consider the following variation of the number matching game. Nature selects an element of Θ^* described by the following probability mass function:

$$\text{Prob}(\theta = 1) = 0.5,$$

$$\text{Prob}(\theta = 2) = 0.5.$$

After nature chooses the true value of θ according to the above distribution, the engineer performs the following experiment. If the true value of θ is denoted by $\hat{\theta}$, the engineer observes a random variable z with probability mass function:

$$\text{Prob}(z = \hat{\theta}) = 0.6,$$
$$\text{Prob}(z \neq \hat{\theta}) = 0.4.$$

The following decision rule is then employed:

$$\text{Prob}(v = 1 \mid z = 1) = 1,$$

$$\text{Prob}(v = 2 \mid z = 2) = 1,$$

$$\text{Prob}(v = 1 \mid z = 2) = 0,$$

$$\text{Prob}(v = 2 \mid z = 1) = 0.$$

In essence, the decision rule selects the most likely estimate of θ and acts as if this were the actual strategy for nature. The expected loss to the engineer if he uses this strategy is

$$\rho = \sum_{i=1}^{2} \sum_{j=1}^{2} H(i, j)\, \text{Prob}(z = i \mid \hat{\theta} = j)\, \text{Prob}(\hat{\theta} = j) = -0.6.$$

When the engineer plays a statistical game as described in the foregoing, he seeks to minimize his expected loss as measured by the cost function ρ. Unfortunately, ρ is a function of both the strategy employed by the engineer and the strategy employed by nature. It will seldom be the case in nontrivial games that a specific strategy for the engineer will minimize ρ for all elements of Θ^*. Thus, he must face the dilemma of choosing a rational basis for deciding upon a single element of Γ^* to be used in a particular game; that is, an appropriate principle of choice must be determined.

Let us investigate explicitly the characteristic of a statistical game which gives rise to this predicament. Player 2 enters into the game with a desire to "win." He wishes to select a strategy in such a way that his expected gain is maximized. The rules of the game provide a format within which it can be determined, after a particular sequence of plays, how well player 2 is doing. Unfortunately, player 2 can measure the effectiveness of his strategy only after the game is finished. The relative value of different strategies for the engineer will almost always be strongly influenced by the strategy of nature, and this is not usually known *a priori*. Hence, the engineer must somehow choose his rule of play without complete knowledge of his opponent's tactics.

The need for a "principle of choice" has given rise to two primary ordering principles, Bayes and minimax. The former is conceptually the simpler and we will examine it first. In a Bayes ordering we assume that nature's strategy is available to the engineer. That is, at the beginning of the game player 2 knows that player 1 will employ the strategy θ_0^*. The expected loss to player 2 of any strategy d^* is given by

$$\rho(d^*) = \int \rho(\theta, d^*)\, d\theta_0^*.$$

To rationally apply a Bayes ordering of Γ^*, one must assume that all of the unspecified elements of the game are random variables with completely known probability descriptions. The engineer is then able to choose his strategy strictly on the basis of minimizing the expected cost, $\rho(d^*)$.

It will often be the case that the strategy for nature will not be sufficiently well delineated to permit the engineer to specify a particular $\theta_0^* \in \Theta^*$ for nature. If, however, the quantity of *a priori* information is enough to determine the free statistical parameters in a previously designated class of probability distributions, and if the cost of the game is insensitive to small variations in $\theta_0{}^*$, then player 2 is justified in selecting a strategy which will minimize the expected value of $\rho(\theta, d^*)$ with respect to the assumed strategy for nature.

In the typical game, however, player 2 is not permitted the advantageous position of knowing his opponent's strategy before the game begins. Instead, both players will have to choose their tactics simultaneously. The engineer now finds himself in a rather ambiguous position because ρ induces only a partial ordering on Γ^* and the best decision rule is not evident from an analysis of ρ alone. If player 2 decides upon $d_0{}^* \in \Gamma^*$ as a strategy, he is certain that his loss will not exceed $\Upsilon(d_0{}^*)$, where

$$\Upsilon(d_0{}^*) = \sup_{\theta^* \in \Theta^*} \rho(d_0{}^*, \theta^*).$$

If we consider nature to be in conscious opposition to player 2, it is clear that if $\theta_0{}^* \in \Theta^*$ is chosen the cost of the process will be at least

$$\Lambda(\theta_0{}^*) = \inf_{d^* \in \Gamma^*} \rho(d^*, \theta_0{}^*).$$

From their definitions we see that

$$\Upsilon(d)_0{}^* \geqslant \Lambda(\theta_0{}^*)$$

for all $d_0{}^* \in \Gamma^*$ and all $\theta_0{}^* \in \Theta^*$.

If the engineer has a cautious attitude toward the game, he may resolve to bound his possible losses with as small a number as possible. Accordingly, he will employ the strategy $d_1{}^*$ (assumed here to exist) defined by the relation

$$\Upsilon(d_1{}^*) = \inf_{d^* \in \Gamma^*} \sup_{\theta^* \in \Theta^*} \rho(d^*, \theta^*). \tag{1.2}$$

In the same way nature may be inclined to insure that player 2 loses as much as possible. Consequently, she will use the strategy $\theta_1{}^*$ defined by the relation

$$\Lambda(\theta_1{}^*) = \sup_{\theta^* \in \Theta^*} \inf_{d^* \in \Gamma^*} \rho(d^*, \theta^*).$$

It is always true that

$$\inf_{d^* \in \Gamma^*} \sup_{\theta^* \in \Theta^*} \rho(d^*, \theta^*) \geqslant \sup_{\theta^* \in \Theta^*} \inf_{d^* \in \Gamma^*} \rho(d^*, \theta^*).$$

If the following stronger condition holds

$$\Lambda(\theta_1{}^*) = \Upsilon(d_1{}^*) = M,$$

then no possible method of play by the engineer can reduce his losses below M with certainty. Similarly nature cannot increase her gain above M with certainty. Accordingly, M is called the "value" of the game, and $\theta_1{}^*$ and $d_1{}^*$ are called "good strategies" for player 1 and player 2, respectively. The decision rule defined by Eq. (1.2) is also called the "minimax" rule, and the principle of choice which results in selecting $d_1{}^*$ as best is termed the "minimax principle."

The minimax strategy has many attractive characteristics in the format of the two-person zero-sum game, for in such a game both players can be judged to be rational beings motivated to increase as much as possible their expected winnings. As we remarked earlier, in statistical games it is rather inappropriate to presume that nature is influenced by possible gain. In statistical games the minimax principle is an indication of pessimism on the part of player 2. He uses no *a priori* information on player 1 at all, but rather assumes nature will act in a manner which is least favorable to him. In many instances this attitude on the part of the engineer will induce him to use strategies which seem rather unsuitable to an impartial observer.

In this section we have presented a somewhat hasty sketch of the fundamental characteristics of two-person zero-sum games and single-experiment statistical games. In both cases the rules and purpose of the game are incorporated in the triple $(\Theta^*, \Gamma^*, \rho)$. This triple along with the principle of choice which is deemed appropriate for the particular game gives player 2 a structure within which to seek an optimal or best strategy. It will be the purpose of the rest of this book to use the special properties of the control problem to aid in the solution to a particular class of statistical games.

4. Relationship of Game Theory and Adaptive Control Problems

In the previous section we have developed some of the basic features of statistical games. The essential thing to observe about these games is that the cost functional is not sufficient to induce a natural ordering on the set of allowable strategies. This same difficulty was experienced in the adaptive control problem analyzed in Section 2. In order to proceed with the design of compensation devices for adaptive control systems we will separate the problem into two parts. On the one hand, we will consider questions related to what should be sought in the way of "good" properties for an adaptive control policy; i.e., a principle of choice is necessary in the adaptive control problem. Second, an adequate synthesis technique must be developed for explicitly determining control policies with the desired attributes.

Let us consider first the characteristics we might look for in a "good" adaptive control rule. If the structure of the system is such that there exists a $\bar{v}_0 \in \Gamma$ such that $H(\bar{v}_0) = \inf_{\bar{v} \in \Gamma} H(\bar{v})$ for all values of the unknown parameters, we would certainly be justified in calling such a control rule optimal. This situation can occur only if the optimal nonadaptive control is independent of these parameters, and consequently, this is a degenerate adaptive control problem. If the ordering induced on the set of allowable controls by H is a function of the unknown parameters, some auxiliary criterion must be used to determine their relative order. For example, when there exists information on the relative probabilities of the unspecified parameters, a Bayes control policy as developed in the adaptive system analyzed in Section 2 might be used. If such *a priori* information is not available, the control system designer might take a rather pessimistic viewpoint and decide that a control policy which minimizes the maximum value of the performance index is optimal.

It is frequently possible to obtain a great simplification in the structure of a control problem simply by eliminating "bad" control policies. By this we mean that if $v_1 \in \Gamma$ and $v_2 \in \Gamma$ and if $H(\bar{v}_1) \leqslant H(\bar{v}_2)$ for all values of the unspecified parameters, then $\bar{v}_2$ is labeled a bad control policy since $\bar{v}_1$ is uniformly better. There is no loss in design flexibility if $\bar{v}_2$ is eliminated from consideration.

In Chapters 2 and 3 the above problems will be examined in greater detail. Here we will utilize game-theoretic results to provide a conceptual framework within which a particular class of adaptive control systems can be imbedded. This study will lead to a definition of what is meant by the adjective "adaptive" when associated with a control problem. It will also permit us to justify some assumptions that have been introduced rather arbitrarily in the past in dealing with control systems whose description is cast in terms of unknown parameters.

5. Synthesis of Optimal Adaptive Control Systems

The purpose of the game-theoretic framework is to provide the engineer with a rational set of goals for his design effort. Having once settled these questions, he must then investigate ways in which to synthesize compensation networks which will realize the design objectives. This is quite a difficult task for plants of a general structure. In what follows we will restrict ourselves to systems which are described by a set of difference equations. Because of this, the system input, output, and control action can be represented as vector sequences. While this is certainly a restriction on the class of control problems which are to be discussed, it appears that most control systems which occur in practice are of a class whose time response can be approximated with arbitrary accuracy by a discrete time model if the time increment is chosen appropriately.

A further restriction on the category of problems which will be considered will be based on the form of the criterion functional. It will be assumed that we are examining a fixed time control problem; i.e., there exists an integer N such that $h(\tilde{x}, v, x)$ is a function of only the first N values of $\tilde{x}$, v, and x.

These two qualifications permit us to use a version of the dual control techniques presented by Fel'dbaum for the synthesis of optimal adaptive controllers. The game-theoretic structure of the adaptive process will permit the application of the dual control formalism in problems in which *a priori* knowledge about the plant parameters is meager.

6. Outline of Book

In this chapter a heuristic discussion of some of the interesting properties of an optimal adaptive control system has been presented. This has been done to illustrate some of the problems which arise when conventional optimal control theory is applied in an adaptive control problem. Chapters 2 and 3 contain an examination of some questions regarding the desirable design objectives when there is uncertainty in the system description. In Chapter 4 is derived a functional equation which the Bayes control policy must satisfy.

Chapters 5 and 6 contain examples of the use of the theory and techniques of the first four chapters. In Chapter 5 difficulties related to the conceptual formulation of a practical problem are stressed. The example studied here illustrates the predicament of the design engineer when the *a priori* information on the plant characteristics is scarce. In Chapter 6, on the other hand, the problem formulation is quite simple but computational difficulties occur in application of the theory. Here, the engineer must be content with a suboptimal control policy. This chapter also explores the relationship between "identification" and "optimization" in adaptive control problems.

Chapter 7 concludes this volume with a brief review of the results obtained herein.

Discussion

SECTION 1. For a discussion of some of the basic structural properties of the optimal control problem see Friedland [1]. One of several papers on the existence of an optimal control policy is Markus and Lee [2]. Some of the difficulties in evaluating an optimal control policy are illustrated in Letov [3, 4] and Krasovskii and Letov [5]. Fel'dbaum's forthcoming book [6] contains an excellent presentation of many aspects of optimal control theory.

SECTION 3. A much more complete discussion of game theory can be found in Blackwell and Girshick [7]. Of particular interest in this reference is Chapter 3, "General Structure of Statistical Games." Further discussions of game theory will be found in Wald [8], Ferguson [9], and Raiffa and Schlaifer [10].

SECTION 4. See also Drenick and Dorato [11].

SECTION 5. See Fel'dbaum [12].

Bibliography

1. B. Friedland, "Optimal Control of Discrete Time Processes," Preprints of the 1963 Joint Automatic Control Conference, paper V-2.
2. L. Markus and E. B. Lee, "On the Existence of Optimal Controls," *ASME Journal of Basic Engineering*, Vol. 84, No. 1, pp. 13–20 (March 1962).
3. A. M. Letov, "The Analytical Design of Control Systems," *Automation and Remote Control*, Vol. 22, No. 4, pp. 363–372 (April 1961).

4. A. M. Letov, "The Analytical Design of Controls: V, Further Developments in the Problem," *Automation and Remote Control*, Vol. 23, No. 11, pp. 1319–1327 (November 1962).
5. N. N. Krasovskii and A. M. Letov, "The Theory of Analytical Design at Controllers," *Automation and Remote Control*, Vol. 23, No. 6, pp. 644–656 (June 1962).
6. A. A. Fel'dbaum, *Optimal Control Systems*, Academic Press, New York, 1966.
7. D. Blackwell and M. A. Girshick, *Theory of Games and Statistical Decisions*, Wiley, New York, 1954.
8. A. Wald, *Statistical Decision Functions*, Wiley, New York, 1950.
9. T. Ferguson, unpublished notes, UCLA, 1963.
10. H. Raiffa, and R. Schlaifer, *Applied Statistical Decision Theory*, Division of Research, Graduate School of Business Administration, Harvard University, Boston, 1961.
11. R. Drenick and P. Dorato, "Optimality, Insensitivity and Game Theory," Presented at the International Symposium on Sensitivity Analysis, Dubrovnik, Yugoslavia, September 1964.
12. A. A. Fel'dbaum, "Dual Control Theory 2," *Automation and Remote Control*, Vol. 21, No. 11, pp. 1033–1039 (November 1960).

CHAPTER 2

A Game-Theoretic Approach to the Formulation of Adaptive Control Problems

1. System Description and Basic Definitions

In the first chapter we indicated with an example some of the problems involved in attempting to evaluate an optimal adaptive control rule for a specific system. Before this synthesis problem is investigated in more detail, it is necessary to spend the next two chapters in an analysis of the fundamental properties of an adaptive control system. Therefore, instead of considering the characteristics of the particular control policies which are optimal for specific systems, this chapter will deal with a fairly general system configuration, and will develop some results on the basic structure of optimal control policies for such systems.

Let the fixed element of the control system be described by the set of equations:

$$\begin{aligned} x_{j+1} &= f_j(x_j\,, v_j\,, \xi_j), \qquad j = 0, ..., N, \\ x_0 &= x(0), \end{aligned} \tag{2.1}$$

where

x_j = the n-dimensional state vector at time $t = j\Delta$. Δ is the unit increment of time;

v_j = the k-dimensional control action vector at time $t = j\Delta$;

ξ_j = the r-dimensional disturbance vector at time $t = j\Delta$.

We will assume that the object of the control action is to cause the plant state vector, x_j, to follow a random command input vector, $\tilde{x}_j$, generated by the equation

$$\begin{aligned} \tilde{x}_{j+1} &= g_j(\tilde{x}_j\,, \xi_j), \qquad 0 \leqslant j \leqslant N - 1, \\ \tilde{x}_0 &= \tilde{x}(0), \end{aligned} \tag{2.2}$$

where

$\tilde{x}_j =$ the m-dimensional command input vector at time $t = j\Delta$.

The performance of the system is to be measured by a nonnegative functional of both the systems' ability to follow the command input and also the control action in the time interval $[0, N\Delta]$. Let x denote $[x_0, x_1, ..., x_N]$; x is the space-time matrix of the state of the system. Similarly, v, $\tilde{x}$, and ξ will represent the space-time matrices of the appropriate variable. Then the scalar valued criterion of performance will be denoted by $h(x, v, \tilde{x})$. For example, if $m = n$, we might choose

$$h(x, v, \tilde{x}) = \sum_{i=0}^{N} (x_i - \tilde{x}_i)^T Q (x_i - \tilde{x}_i) + v_i^T R v_i .$$

The engineer must choose a compensation element which will keep the cost of the control process as small as possible. Because of the design constraints imposed on the system, the control action at time $j\Delta$ must be chosen from a set of allowable control actions; that is, $v_j \in V_j$ where V_j will be taken to be a closed convex set in E_k. The symbol E_k will be used to represent Euclidian k-dimensional space.

In a feedback control system the choice of control action is made on the basis of measurements of system response. In the discrete time case this data will take the form of a vector composed of the observed plant variables. For example, it might contain the input sequence $\{\tilde{x}_0, \tilde{x}_1, ..., \tilde{x}_j\}$ and past control actions $\{v_0, ..., v_{j-1}\}$. We will say that at time $j\Delta$, the controller can observe the vector

$$\begin{aligned} z_j &= r_j(x_j, \tilde{x}_j, v_{j-1}, z_{j-1}, \xi_j), \qquad 0 \geqslant j \geqslant N, \\ z_{-1} &= z(-1). \end{aligned} \tag{2.3}$$

The quantity $z(-1)$ denotes the dummy observation which corresponds to no information at all. Thus, if an open loop control system is analyzed in which the command input is measured through a noisy channel, we might have

$$z_j = \begin{bmatrix} \tilde{x}_j + \eta_j \\ z_{j-1} \end{bmatrix}$$

where η_j is one component of the disturbance vector ξ_j.

Let us now define two spaces of interest in the control problem.

Definition 2.1. Let the $(N+1)$-fold Cartesian product of V_j sets $(V_0 \times V_1 \times \cdots \times V_N)$ be denoted by V.

Definition 2.2. Let the range of z_j be given by Z_j. Then, $(Z_0 \times Z_1 \times \cdots \times Z_N)$ will be denoted by Z.

Since the control action can depend only on the observation vector z_j, the control action can be written

$$v_j = \bar{u}_j(z_j). \tag{2.4}$$

Definition 2.3. Denote by Γ the set of all (measurable) functions from Z to V which have the property described by Eq. (2.4). Any element of Γ will be called a pure control policy and will be denoted by $\bar{u}$ or $\bar{v}$.

In this formulation, the vector ξ_j has been used to account for the random or unknown elements in the system description at time $j\Delta$. It will be assumed that ξ has a probability distribution function of the form $F(\xi_0, \xi_1, ..., \xi_N \mid \theta)$ where θ is an element of a known parameter set Θ and is the essential unknown quantity in the system description.

Following the usual formalism of optimal control theory, we might seek an optimal $\bar{u} \in \Gamma$ by finding the one which minimizes $h(x, \bar{u}(z), \tilde{x})$. This approach quickly encounters the difficulty that $h(x, \bar{u}(z), \tilde{x})$ is a random number. In many situations it is appropriate to use the expected value of the criterion functional as a performance index. Thus, we define

$$H(\bar{u}, \theta) = E\{h(x, \bar{u}(z), \tilde{x})\}. \tag{2.5}$$

Equation (2.5) illustrates the essential difference between the typical optimal control problem and what we have decided to call the optimal adaptive problem. In the former case Θ contains only one element $\{\theta_0\}$. $H(\bar{u}, \theta_0)$ is a function only of $\bar{u}$ if θ_0 is fixed, and thus, it induces a total ordering on Γ. On the other hand, if Θ contains several elements, the ordering induced on Γ may be only a partial ordering.

Definition 2.4. For a system as described above, we will say that the control problem is adaptive if Θ contains more than one element.

If this definition of an adaptive control problem is accepted as satisfactory, we see that the essential thing which makes a system adaptive is an incomplete characterization of some portion of the loop. The definition is not phrased in terms of such operations as "identification" or "learning" because, as will be seen, these operations are difficult to specify precisely in the adaptive situation. Thus, in the example of Chapter 1 no "learning" took place since we dealt with a single-stage process, but this system is adaptive by Definition 2.4. Of course, in a multistage process there will usually occur terms in the optimal control policy which we can attribute to "identification."

In order to proceed further in the investigation of these systems we will find it useful to introduce additional game-theoretic definitions.

Definition 2.5. Let the set of all probability distributions over elements of Θ be denoted by Θ^*. An element of Θ^* will be denoted by θ^*.

Definition 2.6. Let the set of all probability distributions over elements of Γ be denoted by Γ^*. An element of Γ^* is a randomized control policy and will be denoted by u^* or v^*.

Elements of Θ^* correspond to the *a priori* knowledge about the relative probabilities of elements of Θ which the engineer has at his disposal when the control process is initiated. For example, if Θ is the interval $[a, b]$, and if the control system designer feels that all of the elements of Θ are equally likely, then he might choose

$$\begin{aligned} \theta^* &= 1, & \theta &> b, \\ &= \frac{\theta - a}{b - a}, & a &< \theta \leqslant b, \\ &= 0, & \theta &\leqslant a. \end{aligned}$$

The idea of using Γ^* as the space of allowable control strategies may seem unusual to control system designers. With the exception of the work initiated by Fel'dbaum, it has been common practice to implicitly restrict the set of possible control strategies to Γ. To each element of Γ there corresponds a degenerate distribution in Γ^*, and thus, Γ can be viewed as a "proper subset" of Γ^*. Clearly then, use of control policies in Γ^* permits more flexibility on the part of the control system engineer than a restriction to Γ. The question of the utility of this added flexibility will be explored in the sequel.

Definition 2.7. Let $u_0^* \in \Gamma^*$ and $\theta_0^* \in \Theta^*$. Then

$$H(u_0^*, \theta) = \int H(\bar{u}, \theta)\, du_0^*,$$

and

$$H(u_0^*, \theta_0^*) = \int H(u_0^*, \theta)\, d\theta_0^*.$$

Note that the same symbol is used to represent the expected cost for both pure and random strategies. This is done for notational convenience since Θ and Γ can be treated as if they were subsets of Θ^* and Γ^*.

The adaptive control problem differs from the nonadaptive problem in the sense that the performance index does not provide a total ordering of the control policies. Two possible ways of inducing such an ordering are provided by the following definitions.

Definition 2.8. If $\theta_0^* \in \Theta^*$ and $u_0^* \in \Gamma^*$, then define the Bayes cost of u_0^* with respect to θ_0^* as $H(u_0^*, \theta_0^*)$. If there exists a $u_0^* \in \Gamma^*$ such that

$$H(u_0^*, \theta_0^*) = \inf_{u^* \in \Gamma^*} H(u^*, \theta_0^*),$$

then u_0^* is called a Bayes control policy with respect to θ_0^*.

Definition 2.9. $\sup_{\theta^* \in \Theta^*} H(u_0^*, \theta^*)$ is called the max-cost of u_0^*. If there exists a u_0^* such that

$$\sup_{\theta^* \in \Theta^*} H(u_0^*, \theta^*) = \inf_{u^* \in \Gamma^*} \sup_{\theta^* \in \Theta^*} H(u^*, \theta^*),$$

then u_0^* is called a minimax policy.

The Bayes cost and the max-cost are two possible approaches to the problem of ordering the control strategies. They are appropriate in different design situations. If the engineer has sufficient information on the relative probability of elements of Θ available to him, he may be able to assign a θ_0^* to the parameter θ. In this situation a Bayes control policy seems to possess those attributes which could be viewed as optimal. On the other hand, if no such information is available, the designer may take a "worst case" attitude and try to minimize the maximum possible cost.

It is interesting to note that some basic simplification can be achieved in many control problems without recourse to auxiliary ordering principles. This is done by eliminating from consideration all "bad" control rules.

Definition 2.10. If $u_1^* \in \Gamma^*$ and $u_2^* \in \Gamma^*$, we say that u_1^* is as good as u_2^* if

$$H(u_1^*, \theta) \leqslant H(u_2^*, \theta)$$

for all $\theta \in \Theta$. If in addition there exists a $\theta \in \Theta$ such that

$$H(u_1^*, \theta) < H(u_2^*, \theta),$$

we say that u_1^* is better than u_2^*.

Definition 2.11. The control policy $u_0^* \in \Gamma^*$ is admissible if there exists no $u^* \in \Gamma^*$ which is better than u_0^*.

Definition 2.12. A subset $S \subset \Gamma^*$ is complete if for every $v_1^* \in \Gamma^* - S$ there exists $v_0^* \in S$ such that v_0^* is better than v_1^*.† $S \subset \Gamma^*$ is essentially complete if for every $v_1^* \in \Gamma^*$ there exists $v_0^* \in S$ such that v_0^* is as good as v_1^*. $S \subset \Gamma^*$ is minimal (essentially) complete if S is (essentially) complete and no proper subset of S is (essentially) complete.

Admissibility constitutes a weak sort of optimal property, and seems to be a necessary requirement for any control rule which we might call optimal. The concept of an essentially complete class of control rules is very important in adaptive control theory because if such a set exists which is much smaller than Γ^*, then the control problem may be simplified considerably. For example, if Γ considered as a subset of Γ^* is essentially complete, the number of possible candidates for the optmial control has been reduced significantly. This restriction to Γ is of very great practical importance because the complexity of mechanizing a randomized strategy could be prohibitive.

† $A - B$ signifies a set-theoretic difference; i.e., all those points which are simultaneously contained in A but are not contained in B.

Definition 2.13. Let $\bar{u}_1$ and $\bar{u}_2$ be elements of Γ. Then define

$$\| \bar{u}_1 - \bar{u}_2 \| = \sup_{z \in Z} \| \bar{u}_1(z) - \bar{u}_2(z) \|$$

where $\| u(z) \|$ denotes the Euclidean distance in V.

Thus, we define two control policies as close if the maximum value of their difference is small. In what follows it will be assumed that $H(\bar{u}, \theta)$ is continuous in its arguments.

2. Convex Functions

The restriction that H be continuous in its arguments seems to be a reasonable one in most applications. Because of the nonzero tolerances on the components which will be used to mechanize the controller, the engineer is almost certain that the actual system compensation will differ somewhat from the optimum compensation. Yet, he is satisfied that the system behavior will be adequate if the tolerances are made sufficiently small. Hence, he proceeds under the implied assumption that the performance index is continuous in $\bar{u}$. In the same way, the mathematical model of the plant is usually only an approximation derived either from system measurements or from calculations employing a nominal description of the component parts which make up the plant. To deduce any meaningful results from an analysis of such a model it must be assumed that the system response is insensitive to small perturbations in the model parameters. Consequently, the requirement that H be continuous is a natural constraint.

In some problems it is possible to deduce another attribute of H, convexity. This property arises in the following way. Let us assume that we wish to design a controller which will cause the output of the plant to follow the command input with zero error. This may be an impossible task in the sense that no allowable controller will yield the ideal behavior. Following the usual formalism of optimal control theory, the engineer decides upon a criterion function to measure the deviation of the actual system response from that desired. Perhaps he uses

$$h(x, v, \tilde{x}) = \sum_{i=0}^{N} | x_i - \tilde{x}_i |,$$

if the input and output of the system are scalar time sequences.

The expected value of the cost functional is the system performance index, $H(\bar{u}, \theta)$. Assume θ is fixed and let us investigate the characteristics of H as a function of $\bar{u}$. Since with θ specified H is a function only of $\bar{u}$, we can seek that $\bar{u} \in \Gamma$ which causes a minimum of H. If the minimum exists, let a minimizing $\bar{u}$ be labeled $\bar{u}_0$. Let $\gamma\bar{v}$ be a control policy of small norm. If we define the addition operator in Γ in the obvious way, it is evident that

$$H(\bar{u}_0 + \gamma\bar{v}, \theta) \geqslant H(\bar{u}_0, \theta).$$

The scalar γ is proportional to the distance between $\bar{u}_0 + \gamma\bar{v}$ and the optimal control policy. As γ increases, we might surmise that $H(\bar{u}_0 + \gamma\bar{v}, \theta)$ increases also since a control policy is being used which differs more and more from optimum. In fact in some situations the performance measure will satisfy the relation

$$H(\beta\bar{u} + (1 - \beta)\bar{v}, \theta) \leqslant \beta H(\bar{u}, \theta) + (1 - \beta)H(\bar{v}, \theta)$$

for all $\beta \in [0, 1]$. Such a function is called convex.

The following lemma will prove useful in situations in which H is convex in $\bar{u}$.

Lemma 2.1. (Jensen's Inequality). *Let $f(x)$ be a convex, real valued function defined on a nonempty convex subset S of E_k and let r be a k-dimensional random vector with finite expectation, $E\{r\}$, for which* $\text{Prob}(r \in S) = 1$. *Then*

(*a*) $E\{r\} \in S$

and

(*b*) $f(E\{r\}) \leqslant E\{f(r)\}$.

Proof. Consider first the proof that $E\{r\} \in S$. This is obviously true if $k = 0$ since S is a point. Assume that the result is true if $k = j$ but that there exists a $(j + 1)$-dimensional random vector which satisfies the hypothesis of the theorem and is such that $E\{r\} \notin S$. Then $E\{r\}$ and S are disjoint convex sets in E_{j+1} and by the separating hyperplane theorem there exists a vector $p \in E_{j+1}$ such that

$$p^T E\{r\} \leqslant p^T r \qquad \text{for all} \quad r \in S.$$

The term p^T represents the transposed $(j+1)$-dimensional vector. Since $\text{Prob}(p^T r \geqslant p^T E\{r\}) = 1$ and $E\{p^T r\} = p^T E\{r\}$, then it must be true that $\text{Prob}(p^T r = p^T E\{r\}) = 1$. Consequently, with probability one r is contained in the hyperplane

$$p^T r = p^T E\{r\}.$$

Let $S' = S \cap \{r \mid p^T r = p^T E\{r\}\}$. S' is a convex subset of E_j for which $\text{Prob}\{r \in S'\} = 1$ and $E\{r\} \in S'$. Thus,

$$E\{r\} \in S.$$

Consider next the following two sets in E_k :

$$S_1 = \{(x_1, x_2) \mid x_1 \in S \quad \text{and} \quad x_2 \geqslant f(x_1)\},$$
$$S_2 = \{(x_1, x_2) \mid x_1 = E\{r\}, \quad x_2 < f(E\{r\})\}.$$

These sets are both convex since they are product sets with convex components and they are disjoint because of the manner in which the second component is specified. Hence, there exists a

$$p = (p_1, p_2, \ldots, p_{k+1})^T \in E_{k+1}$$

such that

$$p^T x \geqslant \sum_{i=1}^{k} p_i E\{r_i\} + p_{k+1}\omega \tag{2.6}$$

for all $x \in S_1$ where $\omega < f(E\{r\})$. Since ω is unbounded below, $p_{k+1} \geqslant 0$. Because of the continuity of the inner product in E_{k+1}, it follows from Eq. (2.6) that

$$\sum_{i=1}^{k} p_i(r_i - E\{r_i\}) + f(r)p_{k+1} \geqslant p_{k+1} f(E\{r\}). \tag{2.7}$$

If we assume that $E\{r_i\}$ is an interior point of S, then for each $p_i \neq 0$ there exists an $r_i \in S$ such that $p_i(r_i - E\{r_i\}) < 0$. Hence, $p_{k+1} > 0$ if Eq. (2.7) is to be satisfied. Taking the expected value of both sides of Eq. (2.7), we see that

$$E\{f(r)\} \geqslant f(E\{r\}).$$

If $E\{r\}$ is not an interior point of S, it must be a boundary point. Then the probability distribution over S gives all of its measure to a subset of dimension less than k. For this case an induction argument like that presented in the first part of the theorem can be used to verify that it is still true that $E\{f(r)\} \geqslant f(E\{r\})$. ▼[†]

Before we leave this brief discussion of convexity it would be well to illustrate the application of Jensen's inequality. Consider the game in which the engineer selects a real number x from E_1 and pays to nature the amount $f(x)$. Obviously, his best strategy is to choose that $x \in E_1$ which minimizes $f(x)$. This requires a rather detailed knowledge of $f(x)$. Lacking this knowledge, suppose that an observer proposes that the engineer employ a randomized strategy in which x is selected according to the probability distribution function Nor(θ, σ^2). Then, knowing only that $f(x)$ is measurable and convex, the engineer can state with certainty that the pure strategy $x = \theta$ is as good as the randomized strategy which was put forth by the spectator.

3. Some General Results

In Section 1 we presented the definition of an (essentially) complete class of control policies. It is important to investigate conditions under which some appropriately chosen proper subset of Γ^* is (essentially) complete since this means that only control policies in some proper subset of Γ^* need be considered in finding optimal control policies. From the previous definitions it is clear that some relations exist between complete classes of control rules and admissible control rules. One such relation can be stated as follows.

Theorem 2.1. *If a minimal complete class of control policies exists, it consists of exactly the admissible policies.*

Proof. Let $C \subset \Gamma^*$ be a minimal complete class and let $A \subset \Gamma^*$ be the set of admissible policies. Let $B_1 = A - C$. If $v_1^* \in B_1$, then there exists a $v_2^* \in C$ such that v_2^* is better than v_1^*. But then v_1^* is not admissible. This is a contradiction since $v_1^* \in A$. Therefore, $B_1 = \phi$ and $A \subset C$.

[†] The symbol ▼ signifies "end of proof."

Let $B_2 = C - A$ and let $v_1^* \in B_2$. By hypothesis v_1^* is not admissible. Thus, there exists a $v_2^* \in \Gamma^*$ such that v_2^* is better than v_1^*. Since C is complete either (1) $v_2^* \in C$ or (2) there exists a $v_3^* \in C$ such that v_3^* is better than v_2^*. Let $C_1 = C - \{v_1^*\}$. Then C_1 is complete since $C_1 \subset C$ and, therefore, for every rule in $\Gamma^* - C$ there exists a better rule in C_1. This is a contradiction to the assertion that C is minimal complete. Thus, $B_2 = \phi$, and $A = C$. ▼

Consequently, a minimal complete class will contain all of the "good" control policies. While the results of Theorem 2.1 are of interest in gaining a conceptual feeling for the adaptive control problem, they do not appear to be very practical in the sense of aiding the designer in the synthesis of compensation networks. This follows from the fact that a minimal complete class is usually very difficult to find with direct methods. We can, however, make very significant practical simplifications in the problem structure by deriving some results which relate to essentially complete classes.

Theorem 2.2. *If $H(\bar{v}, \theta)$ is convex in $\bar{v}$ and unbounded in $\| \bar{v} \|$, then Γ considered as a subset of Γ^* is essentially complete.*

Proof. Let v_0^* be an element of Γ^*. Let $\bar{v}(z)$ be a random variable with values in V and probability distribution function $v_0^*(z)$. $H(\bar{v}, \theta)$ is a convex real valued function of $\bar{v}$. Since V is a convex set in a finite-dimensional space, Lemma 2.1 can be used to state

$$H(E\{\bar{v}(z)\}, \theta) \leqslant E\{H(\bar{v}(z), \theta)\}$$

for all $z \in Z$. But by definition

$$E\{H(\bar{v}(z), \theta) | \, z, \theta\} = H(v_0^*(z), \theta).$$

Define

$$\bar{v}_0(z) = E\{\bar{v}(z)\}.$$

Since $\bar{v}(z) \in V$ with probability one, $\bar{v}_0(z) \in V$. Then

$$H(\bar{v}_0, \theta) \leqslant H(v_0^*, \theta).$$

Since this is true for all $\theta \in \Theta$, $\bar{v}_0$ viewed as an element of Γ^* is as good as v_0^*. But for every $v^* \in \Gamma^*$ we can find a $\bar{v}$ as good. Thus, Γ viewed as a subset of Γ^* is essentially complete. ▼

The result of the preceding theorem is quite important because it shows that only pure control policies need be considered for a large class of problems; that is, given any policy in Γ^*, there exists a pure control policy which is at least as good. It should be noted that this result has usually been simply assumed in the literature on adaptive control theory. Also note that the results of Theorem 2.2 may not be true if the convexity restriction on $H(\bar{v}, \theta)$ is removed from the hypothesis.

4. Bayes Control Policies

The use of $H(u^*, \theta)$ to order the control policies has an obvious deficiency. Instead of leading to an optimal control for the process, it leads to a set of admissible control policies, each of which possesses a rather weak optimality property. This result is not satisfactory in practice because the engineer needs a specific control rule which is best rather than a set of admissible rules. In this section some properties of a Bayes ordering of Γ^* will be investigated.

Every control action $v^* \in \Gamma^*$ has associated with it a set of non-negative real numbers which represent the Bayes cost with respect to various $\theta^* \in \Theta^*$. If it is known that the actual value of θ in the system is a particular realization of a random variable with range in Θ and distribution function θ_0^*, then it seems reasonable to associate with each control $v^* \in \Gamma^*$ its Bayes cost with respect to θ_0^*. If this set of real numbers has a minimum value, then the control policies associated with this minimum Bayes cost can be labeled optimal for the adaptive problem. Before attaching such an adjective to v_0^*, one should investigate the admissibility of such a rule.

Definition 2.14. Let θ be a random variable with range in Θ and probability distribution function θ_0^*. Then the point $\theta_0 \in \Theta$ is in the support set S of θ_0^* if for every $\epsilon > 0$

$$EI_{(\theta_0-\epsilon,\theta_0+\epsilon)} > 0.$$

$I_{(a,b)}$ is the characteristic function of the set (a, b), and $(\theta_0 - \epsilon, \theta_0 + \epsilon)$ is the ϵ ball about θ_0 in the appropriate space.

Theorem 2.3. *If $v_0^* \in \Gamma^*$ is Bayes with respect to θ_0^* and the support of θ_0^* is Θ, then v_0^* is admissible.*

Proof. Suppose v_0^* is not admissible. Then there exists a $v_1^* \in \Gamma^*$ $H(v_1^*, \theta) \leqslant H(v_0^*, \theta)$ for all $\theta \in \Theta$ and such that there exists a $\theta_0 \in \Theta$ such that $H(v_1^*, \theta_0) < H(v_0^*, \theta_0)$. Since $H(v_1^*, \theta)$ is continuous in θ, there exists $\epsilon > 0$ such that if

$$\eta = H(v_0^*, \theta_0) - H(v_1^*, \theta_0) > 0,$$

then

$$H(v_1^*, \theta) \leqslant H(v_0^*, \theta) - \eta/2$$

for all $\theta \in (\theta_0 - \epsilon, \theta_0 + \epsilon)$. Thus, if θ is a random variable over Θ with distribution θ_0^*,

$$E\{H(v_0^*, \theta)\} - E\{H(v_1^*, \theta)\} \geqslant \eta/2EI_{(\theta_0-\epsilon,\theta_0+\epsilon)} .$$

Since the support of θ_0^* contains $\{\theta_0\}$, the right side of the inequality is greater than zero. Thus, v_0^* is not Bayes with respect to θ_0^*. This is a contradiction, and v_0^* is admissible. ▼

Theorem 2.3 provides a very useful result in control system theory. Notice that θ_0^* represents the *a priori* knowledge about the characteristics of the system, and Θ represents the set of possible values for θ. Usually, it will be true that the support of θ_0^* will, in fact, be Θ; for, if the support of θ_0^* is a proper subset of Θ, we are implying that there is prior knowledge which makes some values of Θ very unlikely. In particular, if Θ is an interval or if Θ is a finite set, any reasonable *a priori* probability distribution will have Θ for its support set.

The fact that Bayes rules are admissible under rather mild restrictions on $H(\bar{v}, \theta^*)$ makes the study of Bayes policies important. In the above theorem the problem has been analyzed in Γ^*, but it can be shown that for a Bayes ordering, Γ is essentially complete.

Theorem 2.4. *If $v_0^* \in \Gamma^*$ is Bayes with respect to $\theta_0^* \in \Theta^*$, then there exists a $\bar{v}_0 \in \Gamma$ for which $H(\bar{v}_0, \theta_0^*) = H(v_0^*, \theta_0^*)$.*

Proof. Since v_0^* is a Bayes control policy with respect to θ_0^*, it must be true that

$$H(v_0^*, \theta_0^*) \leqslant H(\bar{v}, \theta_0^*)$$

for all $\bar{v} \in \Gamma$. If $\bar{z}$ is a random variable with values in Γ and distribution function v_0^* and if θ is a random variable with distribution function θ_0^*,

$$H(v_0^*, \theta_0^*) = E_\theta E_{\bar{z}} H(\bar{z}, \theta).$$

Since $H(.\,,.)$ is continuous in each of its arguments and is non-negative, we can interchange the order of integration. Therefore,

$$\begin{aligned} H(v_0^*, \theta_0^*) &= E_{\bar{z}} E_\theta H(\bar{z}, \theta), \\ &= E\{H(\bar{z}, \theta_0^*)\}. \end{aligned}$$

But v_0^* is a Bayes policy, and therefore

$$H(\bar{z}, \theta_0^*) \geqslant H(v_0^*, \theta_0^*)$$

for all $\bar{z} \in \Gamma$. Combining the above equations, we obtain the result that

$$H(\bar{z}, \theta_0^*) = H(v_0^*, \theta_0^*)$$

with probability one. The distribution v_0^* assigns probability one to a set of $\bar{z} \in \Gamma$ with Bayes cost equal to that of the Bayes control rule. Any one of the $\bar{z} \in \Gamma$ for which the above equivalence exists will satisfy the conclusion of the theorem. ▼

This is a useful result because it permits the control system designer to consider only functions of observed data if he uses a Bayes cost as a performance index. It is interesting to see what restrictions on $H(\bar{v}, \theta)$ were used in proving this result. The requirement that $H(\bar{v}, \theta)$ be convex has been intentionally avoided. The continuity requirement was necessary only to show that the interchange of integration was valid. Any other set of conditions on $H(\bar{v}, \theta)$ which would assure the same results could be used equally well.

Thus, we see that Fel'dbaum introduced no essential generality into dual control theory by permitting control policies in Γ^* because he chose a Bayes ordering of the control rules.

Bayes control policies have several desirable properties. In the first place, the Bayes rules seem to use whatever *a priori* knowledge is available for the choice of an optimal policy. They are pure control rules, and thus, relatively easy to mechanize. They are usually admissible. The main reason that they have received so much attention in the control literature, however, seems to be related to the fact that they are easy to compute. It would simplify the control system design problem if the engineer could restrict his attention to Bayes control policies. For many systems it is true that all "good" control rules are Bayes rules with respect to some *a priori* distribution; i.e., the Bayes policies form an essentially complete class.

Theorem 2.5. *If the set Θ contains only a finite number of elements and if $v_0{}^*$ is admissible, then it is a Bayes control policy with respect to some distribution $\theta_0{}^* \in \Theta^*$.*

Proof. Assume that Θ is a set with m elements, $\Theta = \{\theta_1, ..., \theta_m\}$. Define the set S by the relation

$$S = \{(a_1, ..., a_m) | \; a_i = H(v^*, \theta_i); \quad i = 1, ..., m; \; v^* \in \Gamma^*\}.$$

Note that S is bounded from below and closed. Then define the set Q_a in E_m by the relation

$$Q_a = \{b \in E_m \mid b_i \leqslant a_i, \qquad i = 1, 2, ..., m\}.$$

From its definition, S is clearly related to the expected cost of the process for various policies in Γ^*. Each $b \in Q_a$ is, therefore, related to control policies which are as good or are better than the policy related to a. With this correspondence in mind, if $v_0{}^*$ is admissible and if

$$a^0 = \begin{pmatrix} H(v_0{}^*, \theta_1) \\ \vdots \\ H(v_0{}^*, \theta_m) \end{pmatrix},$$

then,

$$Q_{a^0} \cap S = \{a^0\}.$$

S and $Q_{a^0} - \{a^0\}$ can be shown to be convex sets. Thus, by the separating hyperplane theorem, there exists a vector $P \in E_m$ with components $p_1, ..., p_m$ such that for every $b \in Q_{a^0} - \{a^0\}$ and $a \in S$,

$$P^T b \leqslant P^T a.$$

All components of P are nonnegative since if there exists $\tilde{p} \in \{p_1, ..., p_m\}$ such that $\tilde{p} < 0$, then $P^T b$ is unbounded above for proper choice of $b \in Q_{a^0} - \{a^0\}$. Thus, we may normalize P so that $\sum_{i=1}^m p_i = 1$. The normalized P can be considered a probability distribution over Θ. Choose a sequence of $b^n \in Q_{a^0} - \{a^0\}$ such that $\lim_n \sum_{i=1}^m (b_j{}^n - a^0)^2 = 0$. Then for every $\epsilon > 0$ there exists an n such that

$$P^T b^n < P^T a + \epsilon.$$

Thus,

$$P^T a^0 \leqslant P^T a$$

for every $a \in S$. From our definition of a^0

$$\sum_{i=1}^{m} p_i H(v_0{}^*, \theta_i) \leqslant \sum_{i=1}^{m} p_i H(v^*, \theta_i)$$

for all $v^* \in \Gamma^*$. Thus $v_0{}^*$ is a Bayes control policy with respect to P. ▼

We can now use Theorem 2.5 to prove another interesting result.

Corollary 2.1. *If the set Θ contains only a finite number of elements, then the class of all Bayes control policies is complete and the admissible Bayes policies form a minimal complete class.*

Proof. By Theorems 2.1 and 2.5, if a minimal complete class of control policies exists it consists of exactly the admissible Bayes policies. It can be shown that a minimal complete class does exist if the hypothesis of the theorem is satisfied. Thus, the class of admissible Bayes policies forms a minimal complete class. ▼

Although Corollary 2.1 has wide applicability in stochastic and adaptive problems, it clearly does not apply to the case where Θ contains an infinite number of elements such as $\Theta = \{\theta \mid |\theta| \leqslant 1\}$. The class of Bayes policies will not in general be complete for such problems, but, by placing a restriction on the space of observable data and a restriction on V_j which is always met in practice, one can obtain an analogous result. Since this result fits most naturally within the domain of minimax control policies, the explicit proof of this property will be deferred until the next chapter. This important theorem will be stated here, however, for completeness.

Theorem 2.6. *If V_j is bounded for all j, if Z is a finite set, and if $H(\bar{v}, \theta^*)$ is convex in $\bar{v}$, then the class of extended Bayes rules (see Definition 3.1) is essentially complete.*

In several of the above theorems the criterion functional has been constrained by the requirement that $H(\bar{u}, \theta)$ be convex in $\bar{u}$. In the general multistage process the form of $H(\bar{u}, \theta)$ is much too complex to evaluate explicitly, and consequently, the convexity of $H(\bar{u}, \theta)$ cannot be verified directly. For this reason the following lemma is quite important in application of the results of this chapter because it allows the engineer to infer the convexity of $H(\bar{u}, \theta)$ from a convexity property of $h(x, v, \tilde{x})$.

Lemma 2.2. *The performance functional $h(x, v, \tilde{x})$ is convex in v if, and only if, $H(\bar{u}, \theta)$ is convex in $\bar{u}$.*

Proof. The proof of "only if" follows from the following inequalities:

$$\begin{aligned}\alpha H(\bar{u}_0, \theta) + (1-\alpha)H(\bar{u}_1, \theta) &= E\{\alpha h(x, v_0, \tilde{x}) + (1-\alpha)h(x, v_1, \tilde{x})\}\\ &\geqslant E\{h(x, \alpha v_0 + (1-\alpha)v_1, \tilde{x})\}\\ &\geqslant H(\alpha\bar{u}_0 + (1-\alpha)u_1, \theta).\end{aligned}$$

The proof of the "if" statement will proceed by contradiction. Assume that $H(\bar{u}, \theta)$ is convex in $\bar{u}$ but that $h(x, v, \tilde{x})$ is not convex in v. Since $h(x, v, \tilde{x})$ is not convex, there exist a v_1 and a v_2 in V for which

$$\alpha h(x, v_1, \tilde{x}) + (1-\alpha)h(x, v_2, \tilde{x}) < h(x, \alpha v_1 + (1-\alpha)v_2, \tilde{x}).$$

Let $\bar{u}_1$ be that element of Γ which maps Z into $\{v_1\}$; i.e., $\bar{u}_1(z) \equiv v_1$. Similarly, let $\bar{u}_2(z) \equiv v_2$. By definition

$$\begin{aligned}\alpha H(\bar{u}_1, \theta) + (1-\alpha)H(\bar{u}_2, \theta) &= E\{\alpha h(x, v_1, \tilde{x}) + (1-\alpha)h(x, v_2, \tilde{x})\}\\ &< E\{h(x, \alpha v_1 + (1-\alpha)v_2, \tilde{x})\}\\ &< H(\alpha\bar{u}_1 + (1-\alpha)\bar{u}_2, \theta).\end{aligned}$$

This contradicts the hypothesis that H is convex in $\bar{u}$. ▼

In this section we have investigated some of the properties of Bayes control policies. The results provide a strong motivation for the study of the characteristics of Bayes rules even for problems in which *a priori* knowledge is limited.

5. Policies Based on Sufficient Statistics

In a feedback control system the control action signal which actuates the plant will be a function of many variables. In the problem formulation described here, these observed variables were represented by the vector z. It is obvious that the dimension of z_j is a strictly increasing function of j if the compensation element is permitted a memory of past observations. The engineer is then faced with the difficult design problem of realizing a controller with a large memory capacity. This controller must also be able to form complicated functions which may depend on all elements in memory.

In many circumstances it may be possible to avoid large amounts of storage because not all information contained in z_j is relevant to the control problem. Before analyzing the problem of adaptive control, let us turn to the conceptually simpler problem of estimating a statistical parameter. Let x_1 and x_2 be independent random variables selected according to the normal probability distribution function Nor(θ, 1). The scalar θ is assumed to be unknown. The observation vector z is

$$z = \begin{bmatrix} x_1 \\ x_2 \end{bmatrix}.$$

Since a good estimate of θ would use both x_1 and x_2, it seems at first glance that the estimator must retain both x_1 and x_1 in memory.

The joint probability density function of x_1 and x_2 is

$$p(x_1, x_2 \mid \theta) = \frac{1}{2\pi} \exp - \frac{(x_1 - \theta)^2 + (x_2 - \theta)^2}{2}.$$

Let us make the following change of variable:

$$\begin{aligned} y_1 &= x_1 + x_2, \\ y_2 &= x_2. \end{aligned}$$

Since y_1 is simply the sum of two independent Gaussian random variables, the probability distribution function for y_1 is Nor(2θ, 2). It can be shown that

$$p(y_2 \mid y_1, \theta) = \frac{1}{\sqrt{\pi}} \exp - \left(y_2 - \frac{y_1}{2}\right)^2.$$

We now have the interesting result that the probability distribution for x_2 given y_1 is independent of θ. This leads one to suspect that the statistic y_1 carries all the information on θ which is contained in the sample (x_1, x_2). In fact we might conjecture that for any estimate of θ based upon z, there exists one based upon y_1 which is as good.

Let us consider yet another example of estimating a parameter in known class of distributions. If N independent trials are performed with unknown probability θ of success, the observation vector will be an N-dimensional vector with jth component either 1 or 0 according to the success or failure of the jth trial. The sample provides information on how many successes have occurred and in which order they took place. Since the trials are independent, the order seems to have no relation to the true value of θ. It appears reasonable to assume that a one-dimensional observation that conveys to the engineer the total number of successes in N trials is as useful as the N-dimensional vector described previously.

Simplification has been achieved in the two foregoing estimation problems by partitioning the space Z into a union of disjoint sets, S, and basing the estimate of θ on this partition. In these examples the dimension of S was smaller than Z, and estimation of θ based upon the observed element of S seems to hold promise of allowing the engineer to design a compensation device with much smaller memory capacity. To simplify the control problem as much as possible, we are led to pose the following question. Does there exist a partition S of Z such that control policies based upon S are as good as those based upon Z? Of course, the trivial partition $S = Z$ is "as good" in the above sense, but we are interested in obtaining partitions with a structure that permits a substantial simplification in the resultant control policy. To aid in finding such partitions we introduce the idea of a sufficient statistic.

Definition 2.15. Let z be a random vector with a distribution function $P(z \mid \theta)$ which depends parametrically on θ. A real valued vector function T is sufficient for θ if the conditional distribution of z given $T = t$ is independent of θ.

Note that since $v^* \in \Gamma^*$ is a distribution function which depends on a random variable, v^* is itself a random quantity. To indicate this explicitly, the following notation will be used:

$$H(v^*, \theta) = E_z H(v^*(z), \theta).$$

By its definition T carries all of the information on θ which can be gained from the given quantity of data. The following theorem makes this heuristic idea more precise.

Theorem 2.7. *Let $v^* \in \Gamma^*$ be a function of the vector z whose distribution function depends parametrically on θ. If T is sufficient for θ, then the set $D^* \subset \Gamma^*$ which contains the rules based upon T is essentially complete.*

Proof. Let $v^*(z) \in \Gamma^*$. To prove that D^* is essentially complete we must find a $v_0^*(T) \in D^*$ such that $v_0^*(T)$ is at least as good as $v^*(z)$. Define $v_0^*(T)$ in the following way. If z_0 is the observed value of z, then choose z' out of a population with distribution function $P(z \mid T = T(z_0))$. Since T is sufficient for θ, $P(z \mid T = T(z_0))$ is independent of θ. Then define $v_0^*(T) = v^*(z')$. Note that

$$H(v_0^*(T), \theta) = E_{z'}(H(v^*(z'), \theta) | T).$$

Since T is sufficient for θ, the probability distribution function of z given $T = T(z)$ is the same as the probability distribution function of z' given $T = T(z)$. Thus,

$$E_{z'}H(v^*(z'), \theta \mid T) = E_z H(v^*(z), \theta \mid T).$$

Since T is simply a function of z,

$$\begin{aligned} E_T E_z H(v^*(z), \theta \mid T) &= E_z E_T H(v^*(z), \theta \mid T), \\ &= E_z H(v^*(z), \theta), \\ &= H(v^*, \theta), \end{aligned}$$

and therefore,

$$E_T H(v_0^*(T), \theta) = H(v^*, \theta). \quad \blacktriangledown$$

Hence, an engineer need only retain information on the sufficient statistics in order to control the process in an optimal manner. The elements of the set D^* are, however, randomized control policies and the question of whether a class of pure control policies based upon a sufficient statistic is essentially complete must again be studied.

Theorem 2.8. *If $H(\bar{v}, \theta^*)$ is convex in $\bar{v}$, the set of pure control policies D depending only on the sufficient statistic T is essentially complete.*

Proof. By Theorem 2.7 the set $D^* \subset \Gamma^*$ is essentially complete. Let $v_0^* \in D^*$. Let R be a random variable with values in Γ and probability distribution v_0^*. Since the probability distribution of R

depends on z only through T, it must be the case that $E\{R\}$ is a function of z only through T. If the same reasoning that was used in Theorem 2.2 is followed, it is clear that $\bar{v} = E\{R\}$ is as good as $v_0{}^*$. But $\bar{v} \in D$. Therefore, the set of pure control policies depending only on the sufficient statistic is essentially complete. ▼

Thus, we see that if H is a convex function of $\bar{u} \in \Gamma$, the control system designer need only consider pure control policies based upon a sufficient statistic. Unfortunately, it will frequently happen that the optimal adaptive control rule cannot be evaluated explicitly because of computational difficulties. Specific examples of this behavior will be presented later in the book. In this circumstance the engineer may have to content himself with a control rule which is adequate but not optimal. If suboptimal policy is not a function only of a sufficient statistic it may be possible to improve upon it by employing a policy which depends only on the sufficient statistic.

Before investigating this possibility let us consider again the parameter estimation problem.

Theorem 2.9. (Rao-Blackwell). *Let $p(x \mid \theta)$ be a probability density function for a random variable x. Let $z = (x_1, x_2, ..., x_n)$ be a fixed-size sample from this distribution. Let $T_1 = u_1(z)$ be a sufficient statistic for θ and let $T_2 = u_2(z)$, not a function of T_1 alone, be an unbiased estimate of θ. Then $E\{T_2 \mid T_1\}$ is an unbiased estimate for θ and its variance is less than that of T_2.*

From this theorem it is evident that if we make some estimate of θ based upon statistics other than just the sufficient statistics, it is always possible to improve on the estimate by taking the expected value of this estimate conditioned on the sufficient statistic.

An analogous result can be obtained in the adaptive control problem.

Theorem 2.10. *Let T be a sufficient statistic for θ. If $\bar{v}_0 \in \Gamma$, and if $H(\bar{v}, \theta)$ is convex in $\bar{v}$, then the control policy*

$$\hat{v}_0(T) = E_z(\bar{v}_0(z) \mid T = t)$$

is as good as $\bar{v}_0$ if the above expectation exists.

Proof. By definition,

$$\begin{aligned} H(\bar{v}_0, \theta) &= E_z H(\bar{v}_0(z), \theta), \\ &= E_z E_T H(\bar{v}_0(z), \theta \mid T). \end{aligned}$$

But $H(\bar{v}, \theta)$ is convex in $\bar{v}$. Therefore, from Lemma 2.1

$$H(\bar{v}_0, \theta) \geqslant E_z H(E(\bar{v}_0(z)|\,T), \theta) = H(\hat{v}_0, \theta).$$

Since this is true for all $\theta \in \Theta$, $\hat{v}_0$ is as good or better than $\bar{v}_0$. ▼

6. An Example

To illustrate clearly the results which have been obtained to this point, it would perhaps be well to consider an example in some detail. Let the process to be controlled be described by the scalar equation

$$\begin{aligned} x_{n+1} &= ax_n + \xi_n + v_n, \\ x_0 &= x(0), \\ \tilde{x}_n &\equiv 0. \end{aligned} \tag{2.8}$$

Let ξ_n be a sequence of independent random variables such that

$$\begin{aligned} \xi_n &= 1 \text{ with probability } \theta, \\ &= 0 \text{ with probability } 1 - \theta. \end{aligned}$$

We will assume θ to be unknown, and $\Theta = \{\theta \mid 0 \leqslant \theta \leqslant 1\}$. One would like to choose the sequence v_n in such a way that the criterion functional $h(x, v)$ is minimized. In this problem let

$$h(x, v) = |\,x_N\,| + b \sum_{x=1}^{N} x_i^2.$$

The v_n are to be chosen subject to the constraint

$$|\,v_i\,| \leqslant r, \qquad i = 0, ..., N.$$

To fit this example within the structure of the problem defined in Section 1, define

$$V_i = \{v \mid |\,v\,| \leqslant r\}, \qquad 0 \leqslant i \leqslant N.$$

The solution to Equation (2.8) is given by

$$x_k = a^k x_0 + \sum_{i=1}^{k} a^{k-1}(\xi_{i-1} + v_{i-1}).$$

Therefore,

$$h(x, v) = \left| a^N x_0 + \sum_{i=1}^{N} a^{N-i}(\xi_{i-1} + v_{i-1}) \right|$$

$$+ b \sum_{k=1}^{N} \left(a^k x_0 + \sum_{i=1}^{k} a^{k-1}(\xi_{i-1} + v_{i-1}) \right)^2.$$

Clearly $h(x, v)$ is continuous in all of its arguments. To prove that it is convex in v we need only note that if $0 \leqslant \alpha \leqslant 1$,

$$h(x, \alpha v' + (1 - \alpha)v'')$$

$$= \left| a^N x_0 + \sum_{i=1}^{N} a^{N-i}\xi_{i-1} \right.$$

$$\left. + \alpha \sum_{i=1}^{N} a^{N-1}v'_{i-1} + (1 - \alpha) \sum_{i=1}^{N} a^{N-1}v''_{i-1} \right|$$

$$+ b \sum_{k=1}^{N} \left(a^k x_0 + \sum_{i=1}^{k} a^{k-1}\xi_{i-1} + \alpha \sum_{i=1}^{k} v'_{i-1} + (1 - \alpha) \sum_{i=1}^{k} v''_{i-1} \right)^2$$

$$= \left| \alpha \left(a^N x_0 + \sum_{i-1}^{N} a^{N-i}\xi_{i-1} + \sum_{i=1}^{N} a^{N-i}v'_{i-1} \right) \right.$$

$$\left. + (1 - \alpha) \left(a^N x_0 + \sum_{i=1}^{N} a^{N-i}\xi_{i-1} + \sum_{i=1}^{N} a^{N-i}v''_{i-1} \right) \right|$$

$$+ b \sum_{k=1}^{N} \left(\alpha \left(a^k x_0 + \sum_{i=1}^{k} a^{k-1}\xi_{i-1} + \sum_{i=1}^{k} v'_{i-1} \right) \right.$$

$$\left. + (1 - \alpha) \left(a^k x_0 + \sum_{i=1}^{k} a^{k-i}\xi_{i-1} + \sum_{i=1}^{k} v'_{i-1} \right) \right)^2$$

$$\leqslant \alpha h(x, v') + (1 - \alpha)h(x, v'').$$

Thus, the problem as formulated is contained within the class of systems defined in Section 1. From this result and Theorem 2.2 it follows that there is no loss in generality by restricting attention to control policies contained in Γ.

7. Conclusion

In this chapter we have attempted to analyze some of the basic structural properties of an adaptive control process. The system to be controlled is assumed to be a discrete time system with a fixed time of operation. The characteristic of adaptive control theory which distinguishes it from classical optimal control theory is that there may be no control which is optimal in the sense of minimizing the criterion functional for all values of $\theta \in \Theta$. Instead, the ordering induced by the performance index is partial and we are led only to sets of admissible controls. In many problems each admissible rule can be pictured as an optimal strategy for the engineer with respect to a particular $\theta_0{}^*$.

The search for this desired set of controls is made easier by the result that for a large class of systems pure control rules are essentially complete. A similar reduction in the complexity of the memory of the adaptive system was made possible by the proof that pure control policies which are functions only of a sufficient statistic are essentially complete.

For an actual control system the control system designer has need of a particular control policy rather than a set of them. If he has *a priori* knowledge of the system characteristics, a Bayes control rule seems reasonable. Such rules were shown to be admissible and under certain restrictions the set of all such rules forms an essentially complete class.

If the engineer has no *a priori* knowledge of the system, a minimax control policy may seem more appropriate. The properties of such policies will be considered in the next chapter.

Discussion

SECTION 1. For a discussion of admissibility and completeness see Zadeh [1] and Blackwell and Girshick [2]. Examples of control of objects with unknown parameters are found in Bellman [3], Gray [4], Freimer [5], and Aoki [6]. A different definition of "admissibility" is often used in the control-theoretic literature. For example, see Rozonoer [7]. The idea of randomized control policies was introduced by Fel'dbaum [8].

SECTIONS 2–4. The proofs of these results follow along the lines presented in Ferguson [9].

SECTION 5. For a discussion of sufficient statistics and the Rao–Blackwell theorem see Hogg and Craig [10]. Decision rules based on sufficient statistics are investigated in Blackwell [11], Lehmann [12], and Ferguson [13].

SECTION 6. This example was studied in some detail by Bellman and Kalaba [14].

Bibliography

1. L. A. Zadeh, "Optimality and Non-Scalar-Valued Performance Criteria," *IEEE Trans. on Automatic Control*, Vol. AC-8, No. 1, p. 60 (January 1963).
2. D. Blackwell, and M. A. Girshick, *Theory of Games and Statistical Decisions*, Wiley, New York, 1954.
3. R. Bellman, "The Two-Armed Bandit Problem," *Adaptive Control Processes*, Princeton University Press, Princeton, New Jersey, pp. 215–216, 1961.
4. K. B. Gray, "The Relationship between Certain Classes of Discrete Linear Systems," *IEEE Trans. on Automatic Control*, Vol. AC-8, No. 1, p. 69 (January 1963).
5. M. Freimer, "A Dynamic Programming Approach to Adaptive Control Processes," *IRE Trans. on Automatic Control*, Vol. AC-4, No. 2, pp. 10–13 (November 1959).
6. M. Aoki, "On Performance Loss in Some Adaptive Systems," Preprints of the 1964 Joint Automatic Control Conference, pp. 29–33.
7. L. I. Rozonoer, "L. S. Pontryagin Maximum Principle in the Theory of Optimum Systems. I," *Automation and Remote Control*, Vol. 20, No. 10, pp. 1288–1302 (October 1959).
8. A. A. Fel'dbaum, "Dual Control Theory 1," *Automation and Remote Control*, Vol. 21, No. 9, pp. 874–880 (September 1960).
9. T. Ferguson, unpublished notes, UCLA, 1963.
10. R. V. Hogg, and A. T. Craig, *Introduction to Mathematical Statistics*, MacMillan, New York, 1959.
11. Blackwell and Girshick, *op. cit.*, Chapter 8, "Sufficient Statistics and the Invariance Principle in Statistical Games."
12. E. L. Lehmann, *Testing Statistical Hypotheses*, Wiley, New York, 1959, pp. 17–21.
13. Ferguson, *op. cit.*, Section 23.
14. R. Bellman and R. Kalaba, "Dynamic Programming and Adaptive Processes: Mathematical Foundation," *IRE Trans. on Automatic Control*, Vol. AC-5, No. 1, pp. 5–10 (January 1960).

CHAPTER 3

Application of Minimax Theory to the Design of Adaptive Control Systems

1. Introduction

In Chapter 2 we formulated an adaptive control problem in which the set of equations which describe the object to be controlled contains certain unknown parameters. These unknown parameters represent the uncertainty under which the control system designer must determine an appropriate control action for the object. As the process evolves, information about the characteristic of this controlled element will become available to the designer, and this information can be used to reduce the uncertainty. To measure the relative merit of various control policies, one usually has some performance criterion which permits an ordering of the policies. Thus, in a terminal control problem a control policy might be sought which would minimize some positive definite functional of the system state at the end of the process. In an adaptive process the difficulty of determining such an optimal control is compounded by the fact that a rule which is best with respect to the performance criterion is, in general, a function of the unknown parameters of the system. Thus, there may exist a set of controls, each of which is "optimum" with respect to a particular value for the unknown parameters.

This set of control actions is not a satisfactory solution to an actual problem, and some linear ordering within this set of "optimal" controls must be made which will yield a control that is best in some appropriate sense. If one can assume that the unknown parameters are a particular realization of a random variable with known statistical properties, a Bayes cost using the *a priori* distribution seems reasonable as an ordering index. If, however, the only knowledge about the parameters is the parameter set to which they must belong, a control which minimizes the maximum value of the performance criterion (assumed here to be a nonnegative functional) over all values of this set would seem more appropriate. It is the purpose of this chapter to develop some of the properties of these control policies and to derive methods of obtaining them.

2. Minimax Control Policies

The situation which confronts the control system designer is essentially this. He is given the equations of motion of the system, the set Θ, the observation vector z, and a performance index. He is then supposed to select an optimal control policy from Γ^*. Unfortunately, the above information alone is not sufficient to enable him to choose an optimal control rule. If he had *a priori* information on the relative probability of the elements of Θ, then he would seek to find the Bayes policy with respect to the *a priori* $\theta_0^* \in \Theta^*$. Without such information the problem is more complex. In this chapter one possible solution to this difficulty will be investigated. We will be very pessimistic, and we will assume that the values of the unspecified parameters occur in such a way that the system response is such as to cause a maximum of the performance measure. That is, minimax control rules will be investigated (see Definition 2.9).

The minimax policy has a lot of intuitive appeal in dealing with systems for which there is little *a priori* information. It is, however, not without its drawbacks. On the one hand, it seems more reasonable to attribute to nature the character of an indifferent participant rather than an active opponent; that is, it seems unlikely that the true value of θ will be selected just to make the situation difficult for the control system designer. Second, the minimax policy makes use of no *a priori* information at all. Finally, the max-cost ordering may make all control rules equivalent. This occurs, for example, when there is enough freedom in Θ^* to make $\sup_{\theta^* \in \Theta^*} H(v^*, \theta^*) = \infty$ for all v^*. Then the totally ordered set Γ^* becomes an equivalence class.

These apparent anomalies should not be too surprising. After all, we are requiring the control system to work in almost complete ignorance of an important part of the system description. What we seek in such cases is basically a "reasonable" control policy. The adjective reasonable is the rather vague expression of the designer's ideas on what the control policy should look like. The previous paragraph simply indicates that a minimax control will not always be "reasonable" in this sense. In such a case the engineer must use his judgment by either modifying the max-cost ordering in a suitable manner or dismissing the minimax concept completely. The max-cost simply provides a tool which can be used in the design of adaptive control systems when great uncertainties exist on the exact properties of the system.

The use of a max-cost ordering in an adaptive problem leads to the use of the following definitions taken from game theory.

Definition 3.1. If for every $\epsilon > 0$, there exists a $\theta_\epsilon^* \in \Theta^*$ such that

$$H(v_0^*, \theta_\epsilon^*) \leqslant \inf_{v^* \in \Gamma^*} H(v^*, \theta_\epsilon^*) + \epsilon,$$

then v_0^* is called an extended Bayes control policy.

Definition 3.2. If

$$\sup_{\theta^* \in \Theta^*} \inf_{v^* \in \Gamma^*} H(v^*, \theta^*) = \inf_{v^* \in \Gamma^*} \sup_{\theta^* \in \Theta^*} H(v^*, \theta^*) = H,$$

then H is called the value of the adaptive process.

Definition 3.3. If there exists an element $\theta_0^* \in \Theta^*$ such that

$$\inf_{v^* \in \Gamma^*} H(v^*, \theta_0^*) = \sup_{\theta^* \in \Theta^*} \inf_{v^* \in \Gamma^*} H(v^*, \theta^*),$$

then θ_0^* is called the least favorable distribution for the process.

The value of an adaptive control process is the counterpart of the minimal cost functional in the dynamic programming formalism. It provides an upper bound on the cost of an optimal adaptive process. The role in adaptive control theory played by the least favorable distribution is clear. It corresponds to the choice for $\theta^* \in \Theta^*$ which is most antagonistic to the interests of the designer.

3. Existence of Minimax Policies

Let us now investigate some of the properties of minimax control rules. The first topic to be considered is a set of conditions that are sufficient to guarantee the existence of minimax policies.

Theorem 3.1. *If the set Θ contains only a finite number of elements, and if $H(\bar{v}, \theta)$ is unbounded as a funtion of $\| \bar{v} \|$, then*:

(1) *The adaptive process has a value.*

(2) *There exists a least favorable distribution $\theta_0{}^*$.*

(3) *There exists a minimax control policy $v_0{}^* \in \Gamma^*$.*

Proof. It is clear that for all $v^* \in \Gamma^*$ and $\theta^* \in \Theta^*$

$$\inf_{v^* \in \Gamma^*} H(v^*, \theta^*) \leqslant H(v^*, \theta^*) \leqslant \sup_{\theta^* \in \Theta^*} H(v^*, \theta^*).$$

Thus,

$$\sup_{\theta^* \in \Theta^*} \inf_{v^* \in \Gamma^*} H(v^*, \theta^*) \leqslant \inf_{v^* \in \Gamma^*} \sup_{\theta^* \in \Theta^*} H(v^*, \theta^*). \tag{3.1}$$

Assume Θ has m elements; $\Theta = \{\theta_1, ..., \theta_m\}$. Define the set S by the relation

$$S = \{a = (a_1, ..., a_m) |\, a_i = H(v^*, \theta_i); \quad i = 1, ..., m; v^* \in \Gamma^*\}.$$

Define the set Q_a by the relation

$$Q_a = \{b \in E_m \mid b_i \leqslant a_i, \quad i = 1, ..., m\}.$$

From its definition it is apparent that the elements $a \in S$ are related to the expected cost of control policies in Γ^*. We can consider, in a heuristic sense, each $b \in Q_a$ to be related to control policies which are as good or are better than the one related to a. Let $\boldsymbol{\alpha}$ denote a vector in E_m, all of whose components are equal to the scalar α. Then define

$$\tilde{H} = \sup\{\alpha \mid Q_{\boldsymbol{\alpha}} \cap S = \phi\}.$$

Then, if $\alpha = \tilde{H} + 1/n$, $Q_{\tilde{\mathbf{H}}+\mathbf{1}/\mathbf{n}} \cap S = B \neq \phi$. Since B is nonempty there exists an element $a_n \in B$ which is associated with an element $v_n{}^* \in \Gamma^*$.

$$a_n = (H(v_n{}^*, \theta_1), ..., H(v_n{}^*, \theta_m)).$$

Thus,

$$H(v_n{}^*, \theta_i) \leqslant \tilde{H} + 1/n, \qquad i = 1, ..., m. \tag{3.2}$$

Consider any element $\tilde{\theta}^* \in \{(p_1, ..., p_m) \mid \sum_{i=1}^m p_i = 1;\ p_j \geqslant 0, j = 1, ..., m\}$. $\tilde{\theta}^*$ is seen to be an element of Θ^*. From Eq. (3.2),

$$\sum_{i=1}^{m} p_i H(v_n{}^*, \theta_i) \leqslant \tilde{H} + 1/n,$$

or

$$H(v_n{}^*, \tilde{\theta}^*) \leqslant \tilde{H} + 1/n.$$

Since this is true for all $\tilde{\theta}^*$,

$$\begin{aligned}\inf_{v^* \in \Gamma^*} \sup_{\theta^* \in \Theta^*} H(v^*, \theta^*) &\leqslant \sup_{\theta^* \in \Theta^*} H(v_n{}^*, \theta^*) \\ &\leqslant \tilde{H} + 1/n.\end{aligned}$$

Since this is true for all n,

$$\inf_{v^* \in \Gamma^*} \sup_{\theta^* \in \Theta^*} H(v^*, \theta^*) \leqslant \tilde{H}. \tag{3.3}$$

S is the convex hull of the set S_0 where $S_0 = \{a = (a_1, ..., a_m) \mid a_i = H(\bar{v}, \theta_i); i = 1, ..., m;$ for some $\bar{v} \in \Gamma\}$. From its definition the interior of $Q_{\tilde{\mathbf{H}}}$ (denoted by $\operatorname{int} Q_{\tilde{\mathbf{H}}}$) is also convex; that is, if $b \in Q_{\tilde{\mathbf{H}}}$ and $c \in Q_{\tilde{\mathbf{H}}}$, then for all $\beta \in [0, 1]$

$$\beta b_i + (1 - \beta) c_i \leqslant \tilde{H}, \qquad i = 1, ..., m.$$

Consequently, $\operatorname{int} Q_{\tilde{\mathbf{H}}}$ and S are convex sets. They are also disjoint, and it follows that there exists a nonzero vector $P \in E_m$ such that for every b $\operatorname{int} Q_{\tilde{\mathbf{H}}}$ and $a \in S$,

$$P^T b < P^T a.$$

All of the components of P are nonnegative since if there exists $p_\alpha \in \{p_1, ..., p_m\}$ such that $p_\alpha < 0$, then $P^T b$ is unbounded above for proper choice of $b \in \operatorname{int} Q_{\tilde{\mathbf{H}}}$. We may normalize P so that $\sum_{i=1}^m p_i = 1$. Hence, $P \in \Theta^*$ and one can write $P = \tilde{\theta}_1{}^*$. From the definition of $Q_{\tilde{\mathbf{H}}}$, if $b \in \operatorname{int} Q_{\tilde{\mathbf{H}}}$, then $b_i \leqslant \tilde{H}, i = 1, ..., m$. Choose a sequence $b^n \in \operatorname{int} Q_{\tilde{\mathbf{H}}}$ such that $\lim_{n \to \infty} \| b^n - \tilde{\mathbf{H}} \| = 0$. By the continuity of the inner product

$$\begin{aligned}\tilde{H} &= \tilde{\theta}_1^{*T} \tilde{\mathbf{H}} \\ &= \lim_{n \to \infty} \tilde{\theta}_1^{*T} b^n \\ &\leqslant \tilde{\theta}_1^{*T} a\end{aligned}$$

for all $a \in S$. Thus, for every $v^* \in \Gamma^*$

$$\tilde{H} \leqslant \sum_{i=1}^m p_i H(v^*, \theta_i) \tag{3.4}$$

$$\leqslant H(v^*, \tilde{\theta}_1{}^*)$$

$$\leqslant \sup_{\theta^* \in \Theta^*} \inf_{v^* \in \Gamma^*} H(v^*, \theta^*). \tag{3.5}$$

Combining Eqs. (3.1), (3.3), and (3.5),

$$\sup_{\theta^* \in \Theta^*} \inf_{v^* \in \Gamma^*} H(v^*, \theta^*) = \inf_{v^* \in \Gamma^*} \sup_{\theta \in \Theta^*} H(v^*, \theta^*) = H.$$

Equation (3.4) indicates that $\tilde{\theta}_1{}^*$ is the least favorable distribution. Therefore,

$$\tilde{\theta}_1{}^* = \theta_0{}^*.$$

To prove that there is a minimax control policy, one must prove that

$$\inf_{v^* \in \Gamma^*} H(v^*, \theta_0{}^*) = \min_{v^* \in \Gamma^*} H(v^*, \theta_0{}^*).$$

This can be done most easily by observing that the set of all Bayes control policies is complete (see Corollary 2.1). From Theorem 2.4 we see that the pure Bayes rules are complete. Consequently, to find the lower extremum of $H(v^*, \theta^*)$ we need only consider pure Bayes control policies.

Define the set $D \subset \Gamma$ as follows:

$$D = \{\bar{u} \mid \bar{u}(z) \equiv v \text{ for some } v \in V\}.$$

In essence, D is that subset of Γ which makes no use of the observed data vector. Then define

$$W = \{a = (a_1, ..., a_m) \mid a_i = H(\bar{u}, \theta_i), \quad i = 1, ..., m; \bar{u} \in D\}.$$

It can be shown that if W is closed and bounded then so is S. $H(\bar{u}, \theta)$ is unbounded as a function of $\| \bar{u} \|$ by hypothesis, and since Θ is finite, $H(\bar{u}, \theta)$ is uniformly unbounded. If $M > \inf_{v^* \in \Gamma^*} H(v^*, \theta_0{}^*)$, then there exists an $L > 0$ such that $H(\bar{u}, \theta) > M$ for all $\theta \in \Theta$ whenever $\| \bar{u} \| \geqslant L$. Let Γ_L denote Γ restricted to $\| \bar{u} \| \leqslant L$. Define $D_L = \Gamma_L \cap D$. Then H restricted to D_L is a continuous function over a compact domain, and hence, its range is closed and bounded. S is, therefore, closed and bounded below. We now have the result that

$$\sup_{\theta^* \in \Theta^*} \inf_{v^* \in \Gamma^*} H(v^*, \theta^*) = H(v_0{}^*, \theta_0{}^*) = \inf_{v^* \in \Gamma^*} \sup_{\theta \in \Theta^*} H(v^*, \theta^*). \quad \blacktriangledown$$

Theorem 3.1 proves the existence of a minimax policy for a large class of problems since, even if Θ contains an infinite number of elements, it may often be closely approximated by a model which has only a finite number of elements. If a constraint is placed upon the V_j and Z_j sets, the restriction of the finiteness of Θ can be removed.

Theorem 3.2. *If $H(\bar{v}, \theta^*)$ is convex in $\bar{v}$, if V_j is bounded for all $j \in [0, N]$, and if Z is a finite set, then the adaptive process has a value H, and there exists a minimax control policy $v_0^* \in \Gamma^*$.*

Proof. From Theorem 2.1 and the boundedness constraint on Γ it is clear that the set of bounded pure control policies is essentially complete. Because of the finiteness of Z, they also form a closed bounded set in a finite-dimensional space. Thus, by the continuity of the functional $H(\bar{v}, \theta^*)$, there exists a $\bar{v}_0 \in \Gamma$ such that

$$\inf_{v^* \in \Gamma^*} \sup_{\theta^* \in \Theta^*} H(v^*, \theta^*) = \sup_{\theta^* \in \Theta^*} H(\bar{v}_0, \theta^*),$$

and $\bar{v}_0$ is the minimax policy.

To show that the process has a value choose

$$M < \inf_{v^* \in \Gamma^*} \sup_{\theta^* \in \Theta^*} H(v^*, \theta^*),$$

and let

$$\Gamma_\theta = \{\bar{v} \in \Gamma \mid H(\bar{v}, \theta) > M; \theta \in \Theta\}.$$

Since $H(\bar{v}, \theta)$ is continuous in $\bar{v}$, Γ_θ is an open set in Γ for every θ. Also, every $\bar{v} \in \Gamma$ belongs to at least one of the sets. Thus, $\{\Gamma_\theta\}$ form an open covering of Γ. Since Γ is compact, there exists a finite subcovering, $\{\Gamma_{\theta_1}, \ldots, \Gamma_{\theta_m}\}$, of Γ. Hence,

$$\inf_{\bar{v} \in \Gamma} \sup_{\theta_i \in \{\theta_1, \ldots, \theta_m\}} H(\bar{v}, \theta_i) \geqslant M.$$

Consider now the adaptive process in which $\Theta = \{\theta_1, \ldots, \theta_m\}$. From Theorem 3.1 there exists a least favorable distribution $\theta_0^* = (p_1, \ldots, p_m)$ such that

$$\inf_{\bar{v} \in \Gamma} \sum_1^m p_i H(\bar{v}, \theta_i) = H_M.$$

But $H_M \geqslant M$. Since Γ is essentially complete,

$$\sup_{\theta^*\in\Theta^*} \inf_{v^*\in\Gamma^*} H(v^*, \theta^*) \geqslant \inf_{\bar{v}\in\Gamma} \sum_{1}^{m} p_i H(\bar{v}, \theta_i).$$

$$\geqslant M.$$

But this is true for all $M < \inf_{v^*\in\Gamma^*} \sup_{\theta^*\in\Theta^*} H(v^*, \theta^*)$. Thus,

$$\sup_{\theta^*\in\Theta^*} \inf_{v^*\in\Gamma^*} H(v^*, \theta^*) \geqslant \inf_{v^*\in\Gamma^*} \sup_{\theta^*\in\Theta^*} H(v^*, \theta^*).$$

As was shown in Theorem 3.1, the reverse inequality is always true. Thus, the adaptive process has a value. ▼

4. Relationship between Minimax and Bayes Rules

Both the Bayes cost with respect to a specific *a priori* probability distribution and the max-cost induce a total ordering on the set of allowable controls. In Chapter 2 we proved that in many systems all admissible control rules are Bayes with respect to some *a priori* distribution. Hence, we might expect that any reasonable total ordering of the control rules for a system of this type would lead to an optimal policy which was also Bayes. In this section the relationship between the Bayes and minimax control rules will be explored, and it will be shown that under fairly general conditions a minimax policy is at least extended Bayes.

Theorem 3.3. *If the adaptive process has a value, any minimax control policy $v_0^* \in \Gamma^*$ is an extended Bayes control policy.*

Proof. Since the adaptive process has a value,

$$\inf_{v^*\in\Gamma^*} \sup_{\theta^*\in\Theta^*} H(v^*, \theta^*) = \sup_{\theta^*\in\Theta^*} \inf_{v^*\in\Gamma^*} H(v^*, \theta^*).$$

Since v_0^* is minimax,

$$\sup_{\theta^*\in\Theta^*} H(v_0^*, \theta^*) = \sup_{\theta^*\in\Theta^*} \inf_{v^*\in\Gamma^*} H(v^*, \theta^*).$$

Thus, there exists a sequence of $\theta_n{}^* \in \Theta^*$ such that

$$H(v_0{}^*, \theta_n{}^*) \leqslant \inf_{v^* \in \Gamma^*} H(v^*, \theta_n{}^*) + 1/n,$$

and by Definition 2.9 $v_0{}^*$ is an extended Bayes policy. ▼

Theorem 3.3 gives an important tool for determining minimax control policies, for, in the search for a minimax rule we need only consider extended Bayes rules as candidates. It will later be shown that this result forms a part of a powerful synthesis technique for actually evaluating minimax rules. Another consequence of this theorem is that it enables us to prove an important result on the completeness of extended Bayes control policies. The following theorem provides a strong motivation for the study of Bayes control policies in systems for which there exist very little *a priori* data.

Theorem 3.4. *Under the hypotheses of Theorem* 3.2, *the set of extended Bayes policies is essentially complete.*

Proof. Consider any $v_0{}^* \in \Gamma^*$. We must now find an extended Bayes policy that is as good. By Theorem 2.1, the bounded pure control policies form an essentially complete class. Consider now the criterion functional $\tilde{H}(\bar{v}, \theta^*) = H(\bar{v}, \theta^*) - H(v_0{}^*, \theta^*)$. This functional need not be a positive convex functional, so the existence of a value and a minimax policy does not follow from previously presented work. Note, however, that $\tilde{H}(\bar{v}, \theta^*)$ is continuous, and thus, $\{\Gamma_\theta\}$ form an open covering of Γ just as in Theorem 3.2. Since Theorem 3.1 used the convexity constraint only to prove that there was a compact, essentially complete class, the results of Theorem 3.1 are valid for this theorem also. Therefore, using the same argument given in Theorem 3.2, there exists a minimax rule $v_1{}^*$ and the process has a value with the new criterion functional. By Theorem 3.3 $v_1{}^*$ is an extended Bayes policy for the new criterion functional. But if

$$\begin{aligned} H(v_1{}^*, \theta\,^*) - H(v_0{}^*, \theta_\epsilon{}^*) &\leqslant \inf_{v^* \in \Gamma^*} (H(v^*, \theta_\epsilon{}^*) - H(v_0{}^*, \theta_\epsilon{}^*)) + \epsilon \\ &\leqslant \inf_{v^* \in \Gamma^*} H(v^*, \theta_\epsilon{}^*) - H(v_0{}^*, \theta_\epsilon) + \epsilon, \end{aligned}$$

then

$$H(v_1{}^*, \theta_\epsilon{}^*) \leqslant \inf_{v^* \in \Gamma^*} H(v_1{}^*, \theta_\epsilon{}^*) + \epsilon.$$

Thus, v_1^* is an extended Bayes policy for the original process. But

$$\sup_{\theta^* \in \Theta^*} \tilde{H}(v_1^*, \theta^*) \leqslant \sup_{\theta^* \in \Theta^*} \tilde{H}(v_0^*, \theta^*) = 0.$$

Since

$$\sup_{\theta \in \Theta} \{H(v_1^*, \theta) - \tilde{H}(v_0^*, \theta)\} \leqslant \sup_{\theta^* \in \Theta^*} H(v_1^*, \theta^*) \leqslant 0,$$

v_1^* is as good as v_0^*. For every $v^* \in \Gamma^*$ this construction yields an extended Bayes control rule which is as good. Consequently, the class of extended Bayes control policies is essentially complete. ▼

In Theorem 3.3 we proved that under rather mild conditions a minimax policy is extended Bayes. For some systems we can strengthen this result and state that minimax policies are Bayes. Since minimax rules are an indication that the designer is rather pessimistic, it should come as no surprise that the *a priori* distribution for which the minimax rule is Bayes is the least favorable distribution.

Theorem 3.5. *If the process has a value and if there exists a least favorable distribution $\theta_0^* \in \Theta^*$, then the minimax policy v_0^* is Bayes with respect to θ_0^*.*

Proof. The adaptive process has a value. Thus,

$$\inf_{v^* \in \Gamma^*} \sup_{\theta^* \in \Theta^*} H(v^*, \theta^*) = \sup_{\theta^* \in \Theta^*} \inf_{v^* \in \Gamma^*} H(v^*, \theta^*) = H.$$

Since θ_0^* is least favorable and v_0^* is minimax,

$$\inf_{v^* \in \Gamma^*} H(v^*, \theta_0^*) = H(v_0^*, \theta_0^*),$$

and v_0^* is Bayes with respect to θ_0^*. ▼

From Theorem 2.3, if the support of the least favorable distribution, θ_0^*, is Θ, then the minimax rule, v_0^*, is admissible. This is a rather important property to note because admissibility is certainly a very desirable attribute for any control policy which is to be termed optimal. If there is no least favorable $\theta_0^* \in \Theta^*$, then the admissibility of the minimax policy must be investigated separately.

5. Calculation of Minimax Rules

If one seeks a minimax policy for an adaptive control problem, some means of evaluating such a policy must be available. Theorem 3.5 indicates that if the process has a value and if a least favorable distribution θ_0^* can be determined in some fashion, then the minimax policy can be found by simply evaluating the Bayes control with respect to θ_0^*. Unfortunately, even if the extended Bayes policies are essentially complete, the Bayes policies may not be. Thus, there may be no $\theta_0^* \in \Theta^*$ which is the least favorable distribution. In any case, the problem of finding a least favorable distribution can also be quite complex. The next two theorems give two results which will aid in the discovery of the minimax policy.

Theorem 3.6. *If there exists $v_0^* \in \Gamma^*$ such that v_0^* is a Bayes policy with respect to $\theta_0^* \in \Theta^*$ and such that*

$$H(v_0^*, \theta) \leqslant H(v_0^*, \theta_0^*)$$

for all $\theta \in \Theta$, then

(1) *the adaptive process has a value,*

(2) *v_0^* is minimax,*

(3) *θ_0^* is least favorable.*

Proof.

$$\begin{aligned} \inf_{v^* \in \Gamma^*} \sup_{\theta^* \in \Theta^*} H(v^*, \theta^*) &\leqslant \sup_{\theta^* \in \Theta^*} H(v_0^*, \theta^*) \\ &\leqslant H(v_0^*, \theta_0^*). \end{aligned} \tag{3.6}$$

But v_0^* is Bayes with respect to θ_0^*.

$$H(v_0^*, \theta_0^*) \leqslant \sup_{\theta^* \in \Theta^*} \inf_{v^* \in \Gamma^*} H(v^*, \theta^*). \tag{3.7}$$

Combining Eqs. (3.6) and (3.7) and noting that the reverse inequality is always true, we see that the three assertions of the theorem are clearly justified. ▼

Theorem 3.7. *If there exists a sequence $v_n^* \in \Gamma^*$ with each component a Bayes policy with respect to $\theta_n^* \in \Theta^*$, if* $\lim_{n \to \infty} H(v_n^*, \theta_n^*)$

$= C$, *and if there exists a* $v_0^* \in \Gamma^*$ *such that* $H(v_0^*, \theta) \leqslant C$ *for all* $\theta \in \Theta$, *then*:

(1) *the adaptive process has a value,*

(2) v_0^* *is minimax.*

Proof. By definition of a Bayes policy,

$$H(v_n^*, \theta_n^*) = \inf_{v^* \in \Gamma^*} H(v^*, \theta_n^*)$$
$$\leqslant \sup_{\theta^* \in \Theta^*} \inf_{v^* \in \Gamma^*} H(v^*, \theta^*),$$

and therefore

$$\begin{aligned} \lim_{n \to \infty} H(v_n^*, \theta_n^*) &= C \\ &\leqslant \sup_{\theta^* \in \Theta^*} \inf_{v^* \in \Gamma^*} H(v^*, \theta^*). \end{aligned} \tag{3.8}$$

But for every $\theta \in \Theta$

$$H(v_0^*, \theta) \leqslant C,$$

and we have the result that

$$\begin{aligned} \inf_{v^* \in \Gamma^*} \sup_{\theta^* \in \Theta^*} H(v^*, \theta^*) &\leqslant \sup_{\theta^* \in \Theta^*} H(v_0^*, \theta_0^*) \\ &\leqslant C. \end{aligned} \tag{3.9}$$

If we combine Eqs. (3.8) and (3.9), noting that the reverse inequality is always true, it is apparent that the process has a value and v_0^* is minimax. ▼

The methods for determining a minimax rule given by the preceding two theorems are useful primarily for problems in which one can guess the least favorable distribution or at least can guess a sequence of distributions which converge weakly to some generalized least favorable distribution. A method which circumvents these problems in a large number of processes involves the concept of an equalizer policy.

Definition 3.4. If there exists an element $v_0^* \in \Gamma^*$ such that

$$H(v_0^*, \theta) = C$$

for all $\theta \in \Theta$, then v_0^* is called an equalizer policy.

It is probably not intuitively clear that a control rule with the simple structure of an equalizer could have much importance in adaptive control theory. We will find in the synthesis problems in the following chapters, however, that the use of equalizer policies furnishes a very valuable tool for finding a minimax policy. Basically, this result follows from the fact that in a control system design situation, it may be much simpler to guess an equalizer policy than it is to determine the least favorable distribution function in Θ^*.

The next theorem gives some motivation for our discussion of equalizer rules.

Theorem 3.8. *If the adaptive process has a value, if $v_0^* \in \Gamma^*$ is a minimax policy, and if θ_0^* is the least favorable distribution, then for any θ in the support of θ_0^**

$$H(v_0^*, \theta) = H.$$

Proof. Since v_0^* is a minimax policy and the process has a value,

$$H(v_0^*, \theta_0^*) = H = \sup_{\theta^* \in \Theta^*} \inf_{v^* \in \Gamma^*} H(v^*, \theta^*).$$

Thus $H(v_0^*, \theta) \leqslant H$ for all $\theta \in \Theta$. Suppose there exists θ_1 in the support of θ_0^* such that $H(v_0^*, \theta_1) < H$. By the continuity of $H(v_0^*, \theta)$ there exists an $\epsilon > 0$ such that if

$$\eta = H - H(v_0^*, \theta_1) > 0,$$

then $H \geqslant H(v_0^*, \theta) + \eta/2$ for all $\theta \in (\theta_1 - \epsilon, \theta_1 + \epsilon)$. Consequently,

$$\begin{aligned} \int_\Theta H(v_0^*, \theta)\, d\theta_0^* &= \int_{\Theta - (\theta_1 - \epsilon, \theta_1 + \epsilon)} H(v_0^*, \theta)\, d\theta_0^* \\ &\quad + \int_{(\theta_1 - \epsilon, \theta_1 + \epsilon)} H(v_0^*, \theta)\, d\theta_0^* \\ &\leqslant HEI_{(\Theta - (\theta_1 - \epsilon, \theta_1 + \epsilon))} + \left(H - \frac{\eta}{2}\right) EI_{(\theta_1 - \epsilon, \theta_1 + \epsilon)} \\ &\leqslant H - \frac{\eta}{2} EI_{(\theta_1 - \epsilon, \theta_1 + \epsilon)}\, . \end{aligned}$$

But θ_1 is in the support of θ_0^*, and therefore

$$H < H.$$

This contradiction proves the theorem. ▼

The final result to be presented will prove to be quite useful in the application of this theory.

Theorem 3.9. *If $v_0^* \in \Gamma^*$ is an equalizer and is extended Bayes, then it is also minimax and the adaptive process has a value.*

Proof. Since v_0^* is an equalizer, $H(v_0^*, \theta) = C$ for all $\theta \in \Theta$. Thus,

$$\begin{aligned} \inf_{v^* \in \Gamma} \sup_{\theta^* \in \Theta^*} H(v^*, \theta^*) &\leqslant \sup_{\theta^* \in \Theta^*} H(v_0^*, \theta^*) \\ &\leqslant C. \end{aligned} \tag{3.10}$$

Since v_0^* is an extended Bayes policy, for every $\epsilon > 0$ there exists $\theta_\epsilon^* \in \Theta^*$, such that

$$C \leqslant \inf_{v^* \in \Gamma^*} H(v^*, \theta_\epsilon^*) + \epsilon.$$

Since this is true for all $\epsilon > 0$,

$$C \leqslant \sup_{\theta^* \in \Theta^*} \inf_{v^* \in \Gamma^*} H(v^*, \theta^*). \tag{3.11}$$

If we combine Eqs. (3.10) and (3.11), noting that the reverse inequality is always true, the assertions of the theorem follow. ▼

6. An Example

To illustrate the results which have been obtained, it would perhaps be well to consider an example. The example chosen is quite simple and serves only to clarify the technique. For examples of the use of this formulation in more complex and more interesting adaptive control problems, the reader is referred to later chapters. The system to be considered here is described by the scalar difference equation

$$\begin{aligned} x_{j+1} &= A x_j + \xi v_i , \\ x_0 &= x(0), \\ \tilde{x}_j &\equiv 0, \end{aligned} \tag{3.12}$$

where ξ represents the unknown element of the system. It will be assumed that

$$\theta = \xi,$$

$$\Theta = \{\theta_1, \theta_2\},$$

$$z_0 = x_0 .$$

In this example there are no random elements. This is a system with an unknown parameter and a two-element parameter set. A single-stage process will be analyzed with a quadratic weighting of state. The criterion function is

$$h(x, v) = x_1^2.$$

From Eq. (3.12)

$$H(\bar{v}, \theta) = (Ax_0 + \theta v_0)^2. \tag{3.13}$$

The problem is now to find the value of the process and the minimax policy. It is clear that $H(. , .)$ is continuous in its arguments and quadratic in v. Thus, Theorem 3.1 can be applied to prove the existence of the minimax policy. Since there is no obvious indication as to what the least favorable distribution might be, the equalizer approach of Theorem 3.9 will be used. First consider Θ^*.

$$d\Theta^* = \left\{(p_1, p_2) \mid p_i \geqslant 0, \quad i = 1, 2; \sum_{i=1}^{2} p_i = 1\right\}.$$

The expected Bayes cost of the policies in Γ^* must now be determined. Note that, since $H(. , .)$ is convex in $\bar{v}$, only elements of Γ need be considered.

$$H(\bar{v}, \theta^*) = p_1(Ax_0 + \theta_1 v_0)^2 + p_2(Ax_0 + \theta_2 v_0)^2. \tag{3.14}$$

Minimizing the right-hand side of Eq. (3.14) with respect to v_0, we obtain the Bayes policy $\bar{v}_{p_1}$ with respect to $(p_1, p_2) \in \Theta^*$,

$$\bar{v}_{p_1} = \left(-Ax_0 \frac{p_1\theta_1 + p_2\theta_2}{p_1\theta_1^2 + p_2\theta_2^2}\right). \tag{3.15}$$

From Theorem 3.9, if there exists one of the $\bar{v}_{p_1}$ given by Eq. (3.15) such that the cost given by Eq. (3.13) is constant for all $\theta \in \Theta$, then that $\bar{v}_{p_1}$ is minimax; that is, if

$$\left(Ax_0 - Ax_0\theta_i \frac{p_1\theta_1 + p_2\theta_2}{p_1\theta_1^2 + p_2\theta_2^2}\right)^2 = C, \qquad i = 1, 2. \tag{3.16}$$

Equation (3.16) can be shown to be equivalent to the expression

$$\frac{p_2}{p_1} = \frac{|\,\theta_1^2 - \theta_1\theta_2\,|}{|\,\theta_2^2 - \theta_1\theta_2\,|}\,. \tag{3.17}$$

Substituting Eq. (3.17) into (3.18) and noting that $\Sigma_{i=1}^2 p_i = 1$, one determines after some algebraic manipulation

$$\begin{aligned} \bar{v}_m &= 0 && \text{if} \quad \operatorname{sgn} \theta_1 \neq \operatorname{sgn} \theta_2\,, \\ &= -2\frac{Ax_0}{\theta_1 + \theta_2} && \text{if} \quad \operatorname{sgn} \theta_1 = \operatorname{sgn} \theta_2\,. \end{aligned} \tag{3.18}$$

Since $\bar{v}_m$ is both Bayes with respect to some $\theta_0^* \in \Theta^*$ and an equalizer, it is a minimax policy for this problem. The least favorable distribution is a function of the values of θ_1 and θ_2. For the case where $0 < \theta_1 < \theta_2$, the least favorable distribution θ_0^* is

$$d\theta_0^* = \left(\frac{\theta_2}{\theta_1 + \theta_2}, \frac{\theta_1}{\theta_1 + \theta_2}\right).$$

The value of the process is

$$\begin{aligned} H &= (Ax_0)^2 && \text{if} \quad \operatorname{sgn} \theta_1 \neq \operatorname{sgn} \theta_2\,, \\ &= (Ax_0)^2 \left(\frac{\theta_1 - \theta_2}{\theta_1 + \theta_1}\right)^2 && \text{if} \quad \operatorname{sgn} \theta_1 = \operatorname{sgn} \theta_2\,. \end{aligned}$$

7. Conclusions

In this chapter some of the properties of minimax control rules have been presented. The essential reason for introducing minimax policies is to provide one possible solution to the problem of controlling an object when the *a priori* information on the object's parameters cannot be formulated as an element of Θ^*. The ordering of the set of allowable controls induced by the max-cost is not without difficulties, as we shall see in the sequel, but in many problems it has a great intuitive appeal.

With regard to synthesis of minimax policies, the result given by Theorem 3.9 will prove to be very useful. For example, using the results presented in this chapter, the adaptive system studied in Chapter 1 admits of a very simple solution: $\bar{v}_0 \equiv 0$ is both an equalizer and a Bayes rule. Therefore, it is minimax.

It has perhaps been noted by the reader that all of the examples we have solved to illustrate the theory have been single-stage processes. The basic reason for this is the fact that single-stage processes have a very elementary structure because of the absence of any requirement of "learning" implicit in the control rule. It will be the purpose of the remainder of this book to use the game-theoretic results provided in these chapters to derive a synthesis technique for the design of multistage adaptive control systems.

Discussion

The proofs of these results follow along the lines presented in Ferguson [1]. Further analysis of minimax decision rules is to be found in Bellman [2], Blackwell and Girshick [3], Lehmann [4], Stikhin [5], and Gadzhiev [6].

Bibliography

1. T. Ferguson, unpublished notes, UCLA, 1963.
2. R. Bellman, *Adaptive Control Processes: A Guided Tour*, Princeton University Press, Princeton, New Jersey, 1959, pp. 180–190.
3. D. Blackwell and M. A. Girshick, *Theory of Games and Statistical Decisions*, Wiley, New York, 1954.
4. E. L. Lehmann, *Testing Statistical Hypotheses*, Wiley, New York, 1959.
5. V. N. Stikhin, "Feedback Control Systems with Contrary Interests," *Automation and Remote Control*, Vol. 24, No. 7, pp. 817–829 (July 1963).
6. M. Yu. Gadzhiev, "Application of the Theory of Games to Some Problems of Automatic Control I," *Automation and Remote Control*, Vol. 23, No. 8, pp. 957–971 (August 1962).

CHAPTER 4

Synthesis of Bayes Control Policies for Discrete Time Adaptive Control Systems

1. Introduction

In the preceding two chapters of this book the general structure of an adaptive control system was investigated in some detail. From this analysis it is clear that Bayes control policies have a very important place in the theory of adaptive systems. If the initial data are sufficient to enable the control system designer to assign an *a priori* probability distribution function to the parameter vector θ, then a Bayes rule seems to possess that set of characteristics which would lead the designer to call it optimal. Even if the *a priori* information is very limited, Bayes policies and limits of Bayes policies may form an essentially complete class. In this chapter we will investigate the synthesis of a Bayes control policy for a particular class of criterion functionals.

2. Mathematical Formulation

As before, let the system be described by the set of equations

$$\begin{aligned} x_{j+1} &= f_j(x_j, v_j, \xi_j), \qquad 0 \leqslant j \leqslant N-1, \\ x_0 &= x(0), \end{aligned} \tag{4.1}$$

where

x_j = the n-dimensional state vector at time $t = j\Delta$; Δ is the unit increment of time;

v_j = the k-dimensional control vector at time $t = j\Delta$;

ξ_j = the r-dimensional disturbance vector at time $t = j\Delta$.

The vector function f_j is continuous for all j in the interval $0 \leqslant j \leqslant N-1$.

We will assume that the object of the control action is to cause the plant state vector, x_j, to follow a random command input vector, $\tilde{x}_j$, generated by the equation

$$\begin{aligned} \tilde{x}_{j+1} &= g_j(\tilde{x}_j, \xi_j), \qquad 0 \leqslant j \leqslant N-1, \\ \tilde{x}_0 &= \tilde{x}(0), \end{aligned} \tag{4.2}$$

where

$\tilde{x}_j =$ the m-dimensional command input vector of time $t = j\Delta$.

The vector function g_j is also assumed to be continuous for all j in the interval $0 \leqslant j \leqslant N-1$.

The performance of this system will be measured by a continuous nonnegative functional of the system's dynamic response and the control action:

$$h(x, v, \tilde{x}) = \sum_{i=0}^{N} W_i(x_i, v_i, \tilde{x}_i),$$

where W_i is, itself, a continuous nonnegative functional.

The basic problem is to select control action in such a way that the cost of the control process is small. It is well to consider in detail what the choice entails. When the compensation element generates the control action v_j, it will have available to it a certain quantity of information on the loop response. These data will take the form of a vector composed of sequences of the observed plant variables:

$$\begin{aligned} z_j &= r_j(x_j, \tilde{x}_j, v_{j-1}, z_{j-1}, \xi_j), \\ z_{-1} &= z(-1). \end{aligned}$$

On the basis of the observed data the control element decides upon a control action $v_j \in V_j$; that is,

$$v_j = \bar{u}_j(z_j).$$

The cost of the control process can be written as

$$h(x, v, \tilde{x}) = \sum_{i=0}^{N} W_i(x_i, \bar{u}_i(z_i), \tilde{x}_i).$$

Since all of the arguments of W_i are implicitly functions of the random variable ξ_k, $0 \leqslant k \leqslant i$, $h(x, v, \tilde{x})$ is a random number. In many situations it is appropriate to use the expected value of this number as a performance index. For a given initial state the expected cost can depend only upon the control policy, $\bar{u}$, and the value of the unknown parameter vector θ. Thus, we can write

$$H(\bar{u}, \theta) = E\left\{\sum_{i=0}^{N} W_i(x_i, v_i, \tilde{x}_i)\right\}.$$

In this chapter the synthesis of Bayes control policies with respect to a given *a priori* distribution $\theta_0^* \in \Theta^*$ will be analyzed. If it is known that the actual value of θ in the system is a particular realization of a random vector with distribution function θ_0^*, then the Bayes policy possesses characteristics that one would intuitively look for in an "optimal" control. The Bayes ordering is a mathematical restriction, of course, as evidenced by the elimination of randomized control policies from consideration. This can, however, be viewed as a great practical advantage of Bayes rules since the complexity of the mechanization of a randomized policy could be prohibitive.

3. Evaluation of the Bayes Cost

Before a policy $\bar{u} \in \Gamma$ which minimizes $H(\bar{u}, \theta^*)$ can be chosen, the Bayes cost must be evaluated explicitly.

Definition 4.1. The $(s + 1)$-fold Cartesian product of E_n spaces, $(E_n \times E_n \times \cdots \times E_n)$, will be denoted by X^s. An element of X^s will be denoted by x^s, and will represent the space-time history of the system state vector from time $t = 0$ to time $t = s\Delta$. Similarly, the $(s + 1)$-fold Cartesian product of E_k will be denoted by V^s. An element of V^s will be denoted by v^s and will represent the space-time history of the control action from $t = 0$ to $t = s\Delta$. The history of ξ, $\tilde{x}$, and z will be denoted in the same way.

At any time $s\Delta$, the control action will depend upon the information vector z_s. Assume that at time $s\Delta$ the following sequences were known: v^{s-1}, x^s, ξ^s, $\tilde{x}^s$, and θ.

Then define

$$\begin{aligned} r_s &= E\{W_s \mid v^{s-1}, x^s, \xi^s, \tilde{x}^s, \theta\} \\ &= W_s(x_s, \bar{u}_s(z_s), \tilde{x}_s). \end{aligned}$$

The expected incremental cost at time $t = s\Delta$ is

$$\begin{aligned} R_s &= E\{r_s\} \\ &= \int W_s(x_s, \bar{u}_s(z_s), \tilde{x}_s) p(v^s, x^s, \tilde{x}^s, \xi^s, \theta) \, d\Omega(x^s, \tilde{x}^s, \xi^s, v^s, \theta) \end{aligned} \tag{4.3}$$

where $\int d\Omega(\ )$ represents an integration over the whole region of variation of the argument of Ω.

Equation (4.3) contains a rather unwieldy joint probability density function. It can be decomposed into a product of simpler parts as follows:

$$p(v^s, x^s, \tilde{x}^s, \xi^s, \theta) = p(v^s, \tilde{x}^s, x^s, \xi^s \mid \theta) p(\theta). \tag{4.4}$$

The conditional density function can be factored still further:

$$\begin{aligned} p(v^s, x^s, \tilde{x}^s, \xi^s \mid \theta) = {} & p(x_0, \tilde{x}_0, v_0, \xi_0 \mid \theta) p(v_1, x_1, \tilde{x}_1, \xi_1 \mid \theta, x_0, \tilde{x}_0, v_0 \xi_0) \\ & \cdots p(v_i, x_i, \tilde{x}_i, \xi_i \mid \theta, x^{i-1}, \tilde{x}^{i-1}, v^{i-1}, \xi^{i-1}) \\ & \cdots p(v_s, x_s, \tilde{x}_s, \xi_s \mid \theta, x^{s-1}, \tilde{x}^{s-1}, v^{s-1}, \xi^{s-1}). \end{aligned}$$

Each of the above factors may now be rewritten as a product of conditional density functions in the following way:

$$\begin{aligned} & p(v_i, x_i, \tilde{x}_i, \xi_i \mid \theta, v^{i-1}, x^{i-1}, \tilde{x}^{i-1}, \xi^{i-1}) \\ & \quad = p(v_i \mid \theta, v^{i-1}, x^i, \tilde{x}^i, \xi^i) \\ & \qquad \times p(\tilde{x}_i \mid \theta, v^{i-1}, x^i, \tilde{x}^{i-1}, \xi^{i-1}) p(x_i \mid \theta, v^{i-1}, x^{i-1}, \tilde{x}^{i-1}, \xi^{i-1}) \\ & \qquad \times p(\xi_i \mid \theta, v^{i-1}, x^i, \tilde{x}^i, \xi^{i-1}). \end{aligned}$$

We can write the joint density function of the system variables at time $t = 0$ as

$$\begin{aligned} p(x_0, \tilde{x}_0, v_0, \xi_0 \mid \theta) = {} & p(v_0 \mid x_0, \tilde{x}_0, \xi_0, \theta) p(x_0 \mid \theta) \\ & \times p(\tilde{x}_0 \mid \theta, x_0) p(\xi_0 \mid \theta, x_0, \tilde{x}_0). \end{aligned}$$

If we combine these equations, the joint probability density function for the system variables becomes

$$p(v^s, x^s, \tilde{x}^s, \xi^s \mid \theta) = \prod_{i=0}^{s} p(x_i \mid x^{i-1}, \tilde{x}^{i-1}, v^{i-1}, \xi^{i-1}, \theta) \times \prod_{i=0}^{s} p(\tilde{x}_i \mid x^i, \tilde{x}^{i-1}, v^{i-1}, \xi^{i-1}, \theta) \times \prod_{i=0}^{s} p(v_i \mid x^i, \tilde{x}^i, v^{i-1}, \xi^i, \theta) \times \prod_{i=0}^{s} p(\xi_i \mid x^i, \tilde{x}^i, v^{i-1}, \xi^{i-1}, \theta) \tag{4.5}$$

where x^{-1}, $\tilde{x}^{-1}$, v^{-1}, and ξ^{-1} are dummy vectors. Combining Eqs. (4.3), (4.4), and (4.5) gives

$$R_s = \int W_s(x_s, v_s, \tilde{x}_s) \prod_{i=0}^{s} p(v_i \mid \theta, v^{i-1}, x^i, \tilde{x}^i, \xi^i) \times \prod_{i=0}^{s} p(\tilde{x}_i \mid \theta, v^{i-1}, x^i, \tilde{x}^{i-1}, \xi^{i-1}) \prod_{i=0}^{s} p(x_i \mid \theta, v^{i-1}, x^{i-1}, \tilde{x}^{i-1}, \xi^{i-1}) \times \prod_{i=0}^{s} p(\xi_i \mid \theta, v^{i-1}, x^i, \tilde{x}^i, \xi^{i-1}) p(\theta)\, d\Omega(v^s, x^s, \tilde{x}^s, \xi^s, \theta). \tag{4.6}$$

Equation (4.6) is an expansion of Eq. (4.3) in terms of a group of conditional probability density functions. We can simplify Equation (4.6) greatly through the use of the equations which characterize the system. In Chapter 2 it was specified that the probability distribution function of ξ_i depends only on ξ^{i-1} and θ. Hence,

$$\prod_{i=0}^{s} p(\xi_i \mid \theta, v^{i-1}, x^i, \tilde{x}^i, \xi^{i-1}) = \prod_{i=0}^{s} p(\xi_i \mid \theta, \xi^{i-1}). \tag{4.7}$$

The conditional probability distribution functions which describe x_i, $\tilde{x}_i$, and v_i are degenerate since these variables are functionally dependent on the variables in the conditional density functions. This, unfortunately, causes a slight problem in notation. We will say that

$$\prod_{i=0}^{s} p(x_i \mid \theta, v^{i-1}, x^{i-1}, \tilde{x}^{i-1}, \xi^{i-1}) = \prod_{i=0}^{s} \delta(x_i - f_{i-1}(x_{i-1}, v_{i-1}, \xi_{i-1})),$$

$$\prod_{i=0}^{s} p(v_i \mid \theta, v^{i-1}, x^{i}, \tilde{x}^{i}, \xi^{i}) = \prod_{i=0}^{s} \delta(v_i - \bar{u}_i(z_i)), \tag{4.8}$$

$$\prod_{i=0}^{s} p(\tilde{x}_i \mid \theta, v^{i-1}, x^{i}, \tilde{x}^{i-1}, \xi^{i-1}) = \prod_{i=0}^{s} \delta(\tilde{x}_i - g_{i-1}(\tilde{x}_{i-1}, \xi_{i-1})),$$

where

$$\delta(x_0 - f_{-1}(x_{-1}, v_{-1}, \xi_{-1})) = \delta(x_0 - x(0)),$$
$$\delta(\tilde{x}_0 - g_{-1}(\tilde{x}_{-1}, \xi_{-1})) = \delta(\tilde{x}_0 - \tilde{x}(0)),$$

and where the δ functions are defined by the equation

$$\begin{aligned} \int \Gamma(x_s, v_s, \tilde{x}_s) \prod_{i=0}^{s} \delta(\tilde{x}_i - g_{i-1}(\tilde{x}_{i-1}, \xi_{i-1})) \prod_{i=0}^{s} \delta(x_i - f_{i-1}(x_{i-1}, v_{i-1}, \xi_{i-1})) \\ \times \prod_{i=0}^{s} \delta(v_i - \bar{u}_i(z_i))\, d\Omega(x^s, v^s, \tilde{x}^s) \\ = \int \Gamma[f_{s-1}, \bar{u}_s(r_s(f_{s-1}, g_{s-1}, v_{s-1}, z_{s-1}, \xi_s)), g_{s-1}] \\ \times \prod_{i=0}^{s-1} \delta(\tilde{x}_i - g_{i-1}(\tilde{x}_{i-1}, \xi_{i-1})) \prod_{i=0}^{s-1} \delta(x_i - f_{i-1}(x_{i-1}, v_{i-1}, \xi_{i-1})) \\ \times \prod_{i=0}^{s-1} \delta((v_i - \bar{u}_i(z_i))\, d\Omega(x^{s-1}, v^{s-1}, \tilde{x}^{s-1}). \end{aligned} \tag{4.9}$$

The above equality is to be valid for every Γ which is continuous in its arguments in the appropriate domain.

Suppressing the arguments of the functions given in Eq. (4.8), we can write the expected value of the incremental cost as

$$\begin{aligned} R_s = \int W_s(x_s, v_s, \tilde{x}_s) \prod_{i=0}^{s} \delta(v_i - \bar{u}_i) \prod_{i=0}^{s} \delta(\tilde{x}_i - g_{i-1}) \prod_{i=0}^{s} \delta(x_i - f_{i-1}) \\ \times \prod_{i=0}^{s} p(\xi_i \mid \xi^{i-1}, \theta) p(\theta)\, d\Omega(v^s, \tilde{x}^s, x^s, \xi^s, \theta). \end{aligned} \tag{4.10}$$

In Eq. (4.10) $p(\theta)$ is the probability density function for θ. Since θ is a constant, its distribution function is degenerate at the true value of $\theta \in \Theta$. Unfortunately, this distribution is not known to the control element at time $t = s\Delta$ because θ is by definition the unspecified parameter of the system. Let $p_0(\theta)$ be the density function which corresponds to the *a priori* distribution for θ. The compensation element can form the *a posteriori* density function of θ at $t = s\Delta$ by use of the Bayes formula

$$p(\theta \mid z_s) = p_s(\theta) = \frac{p_0(\theta)p(z_s \mid \theta)}{\int p(z_s \mid \eta)p_0(\eta)\, d\Omega(\eta)}. \tag{4.11}$$

Note that the Bayes formula is expressed in terms of the observation vector z_s since any estimate of $p(\theta)$ which is made by the controller must be in terms of z_s.

An interesting special case of Eq. (4.11) occurs when ξ^{s-1} appears explicitly in z_s and those components of ξ_s appearing in z_s are independent of θ. This may occur through an auxiliary feedback path or perhaps Eqs. (4.1) and (4.2) can be solved for ξ^{s-1}. The importance of this information rests on the fact that only ξ depends explicitly on θ. Under these circumstances all of the rest of the components of z_s become nuisance variables with respect to estimating θ. With an argument much like the one used to derive Eq. (4.10), we can show that in this case

$$p_s(\theta) = \frac{p_0(\theta) \prod_{i=0}^{s-1} p(\xi_i \mid \theta, \xi^{i-1})}{\int \prod_{i=0}^{s-1} p(\xi_i \mid \eta, \xi^{i-1}) p_0(\eta)\, d\Omega(\eta)}. \tag{4.12}$$

Provided that ξ^{s-1} is observable and the system variables at time $s\Delta$ are independent of ξ_s,

$$H(\bar{u}, \theta_0{}^*) = \sum_{s=0}^{N} \int W_s \prod_{i=0}^{s} \delta(x_i - f_{i-1}) \prod_{i=0}^{s} \delta(\tilde{x}_i - g_{i-1}) \prod_{i=0}^{s} \delta(v_i - \bar{u}_i). \tag{4.13}$$

$$\times \frac{[\prod_{i=0}^{s-1} p(\xi_i \mid \theta, \xi^{i-1})]^2 p_0(\theta)}{\int \prod_{i=0}^{s-1} p(\xi_i \mid \eta, \xi^{i-1}) p_0(\eta)\, d\Omega(\eta)}\, d\Omega(x^s, \tilde{x}^s, \xi^{s-1}, v^s, \theta).$$

For the rest of this chapter, the situation described by Eq. (4.13) will be analyzed. We will return to the more general case of Eq. (4.10) in Chapter 6.

4. Synthesis of the Bayes Control Policy

To evaluate the Bayes control policy with respect to θ_0^*, the dual control technique can be used. This approach is closely related to dynamic programming.

Define

$$\alpha_k = \int W_k \prod_{i=0}^{k} \delta(x_i - f_{i-1}) \prod_{i=0}^{k} \delta(\tilde{x}_i - g_{i-1}) \frac{[\prod_{i=0}^{k-1} p(\xi_i \mid \theta, \xi^{i-1})]^2}{\int \prod_{i=0}^{k-1} p(\xi_i \mid \eta, \xi^{i-1}) p_0(\eta)\, d\Omega(\eta)}$$

$$\cdot\, p_0(\theta)\, d\Omega(\theta); \tag{4.14}$$

$$\beta_k = \prod_{i=0}^{k} \delta(v_i - \bar{u}_i).$$

Then,

$$H(\bar{u}, \theta_0^*) = \int \alpha_N \beta_{N-1}\, \delta(v_N - \bar{u}_N)\, d\Omega(x^N, \tilde{x}^N, \xi^{N-1}, v^N) + \sum_{i=0}^{N-1} R_i\,. \tag{4.15}$$

If we minimize the above expression with respect to $\bar{u}_N$, we see that v_N appears only in the α_N factor, and therefore,

$$\inf_{\bar{u}_N} H(\bar{u}, \theta_0^*) = \sum_{i=0}^{N-1} R_i + \inf_{\bar{u}_N} \int \alpha_N \beta_{N-1}\, \delta(v_N - \bar{u}_N)\, d\Omega(x^N, \tilde{x}^N, \xi^{N-1}, v^N).$$

The minimization is to be taken over all allowable $\bar{u}_N$. It will be assumed that α_N and Γ are such that the minimum exists. Define

$$\rho_N = \inf_{\bar{u}_N} \alpha_N\,.$$

Then,

$$\inf_{\bar{u}_N} H(\bar{u}, \theta_0^*) = \int \rho_N \beta_{N-1}\, d\Omega(x^N, \tilde{x}^N, \xi^{N-1}, v^{N-1}) + \sum_{i=0}^{N-1} R_i\,.$$

The above equation can be written in the form

$$\inf_{\bar{u}_N} H(\bar{u}, \theta_0^*) = \int \beta_{N-2} \left\{ \alpha_{N-1} + \int \rho_N\, d\Omega(x_N, \tilde{x}_N, \xi_{N-1}) \right\}$$

$$\times\, \delta(v_{N-1} - \bar{u}_{N-1})\, d\Omega(x^{N-1}, \tilde{x}^{N-1}, \xi^{N-2}, v^{N-1}) + \sum_{i=0}^{N-2} R_i\,.$$

Define

$$\rho_{N-1} = \inf_{\bar{u}_{N-1}} \left\{ \alpha_{N-1} + \int \rho_N \, d\Omega(x_N, \tilde{x}_N, \xi_{N-1}) \right\}.$$

In what follows in this chapter the existence of a Bayes control policy with respect to $\theta_0{}^*$ will be an implicit assumption. If it should happen that the structure of the system is such that not all of the required minimums exist, then the engineer must resort to a suboptimal controller. There certainly exists a controller with a performance measure which is arbitrarily close to the minimum, and such an ϵ-optimal controller is obviously a satisfactory solution to any practical design problem if ϵ is sufficiently small.

With the definition of ρ_{N-1} given above, the following result obtains:

$$\inf_{\bar{u}_{N-1}} \inf_{\bar{u}_N} H(\bar{u}, \theta_0{}^*) = \sum_{i=0}^{N-2} R_i + \int \beta_{N-2}\rho_{N-1} \, d\Omega(x^{N-1}, x^{N-1}, \xi^{N-2}, v^{N-2}).$$

Observe the similarity in form of ρ_N and ρ_{N-1}, and of $\inf_{\bar{u}_N} H(\bar{u}, \theta_0{}^*)$ and $\inf_{\bar{u}_{N-1}} \inf_{\bar{u}_N} H(\bar{u}, \theta_0{}^*)$. Denote that $\bar{u}_j \in \Gamma$ which minimizes ρ_j by $\hat{u}_j$. Then by induction it is evident that the following sequential procedure may be employed to evaluate the Bayes control policy.

$$\rho_{N+1} = 0;$$

$$\rho_{N-j} = \inf_{\bar{u}_{N-j}} \left\{ \alpha_{N-j} + \int \rho_{N-j+1} \, d\Omega(x_{N-j+1}, \tilde{x}_{N-j+1}, \xi_{N-j}) \right\};$$

$$\inf_{\bar{u} \in \Gamma} H(\bar{u}, \theta_0{}^*) = \rho_{-1}; \tag{4.16}$$

$$\hat{u} = \{\hat{u}_0, \hat{u}_1, \ldots, \hat{u}_N\}. \tag{4.17}$$

5. Examples

To illustrate the development of the preceding sections, two examples will be considered here. The first is a stochastic control problem in which there are no unknown system parameters, and the concepts of minimax policies and Bayes policies coalesce into simply an "optimal" policy. The reason for presenting this example is to show how the above work relates to published work on optimal nonadaptive problems.

Let the system be described by the vector equation:

$$\begin{aligned} x_{j+1} &= \phi_j x_j + \Delta_j v_j\,, \qquad 0 \leqslant j \leqslant N, \\ x_0 &= x(0), \\ \tilde{x}_j &\equiv 0, \\ z_j &= x_j\,. \end{aligned} \tag{4.18}$$

The matrices ϕ_i and Δ_j are matrices with random elements. These elements are assumed to be completely described statistically, and therefore $\theta_0{}^*$ is degenerate at the true value of θ, $\tilde{\theta}$. What is more, we will assume that these elements are independent from one time increment to the next, and that the means and covariances of the random elements are finite.

It will be the job of the compensation element to generate the scalar control action v in such a way that

$$H(\bar{u}, \tilde{\theta}) = E\left\{\sum_{j=0}^{N} x_j{}^T Q x_j + v_j{}^2\right\} \tag{4.19}$$

is minimized. Q is a positive symmetric matrix.

For this problem the form of α_k becomes quite simple.

$$\alpha_k = (x_k{}^T Q x_k + v_k{}^2) \prod_{i=0}^{k} \delta(x_i - \phi_{i-1} x_{i-1} - \Delta_{i-1} v_{i-1}). \tag{4.20}$$

Define

$$\delta(x_i - \phi_{i-1} x_{i-1} - \Delta_{i-1} v_{i-1}) = \delta_i\,.$$

Then, if ρ_{j+1} has the form

$$\rho_{j+1} = x_{j+1}^T P_{j+1} x_{j+1} \prod_{i=0}^{j+1} \delta_i\,,$$

we will obtain the following form for ρ_j:

$$\begin{aligned} \rho_j &= \inf_{\bar{u}_j}\left\{\alpha_j + \int \rho_{j+1}\, d\Omega(x_{j+1}\,, \xi_j)\right\} \\ &= \inf_{\bar{u}_j}\left\{\left[x_j{}^T Q x_j + v_j{}^2 + \int \{(\phi_j x_j + \Delta_j v_j)^T P_{j+1}(\phi_j x_j + \Delta_j v_j)\}\right.\right. \\ &\quad \left.\left.\times\, p(\phi_j\,, \Delta_j)\, d\Omega(\phi_j\,, \Delta_j)\right] \prod_{i=0}^{j} \delta_i\right\}. \end{aligned} \tag{4.21}$$

The notation $p(\phi_j, \Delta_j)$ is used to represent the joint probability density function for the elements of the ϕ_j and Δ_j matrices. Let us define

$$\int f(\phi_j, \Delta_j)p(\phi_j, \Delta_j)\, d\Omega(\phi_j, \Delta_j) = \overline{f(\phi_j, \Delta_j)}.$$

The minimum of the quadratic form in v_j of Eq. (4.21) can be found quite simply. The optimal control rule is given by

$$\hat{u}_j = a_j^T x_j \tag{4.22}$$

where

$$a_j^T = -[\overline{\Delta_j^T P_{j+1} \Delta_j} + 1]^{-1}\, \overline{\Delta_j^T P_{j+1} \phi_j},$$

and

$$\rho_j = x_j^T P_j x_j \prod_{i=0}^{j} \delta_i \tag{4.23}$$

where

$$P_j = Q + \overline{\phi_j^T P_{j+1} \phi_j} - a_j(\overline{\Delta_j^T P_{j+1} \Delta_j} + 1)a_j^T.$$

From Eq. (4.20) it is clear that

$$P_{N+1} = 0. \tag{4.24}$$

Thus, Eqs. (4.22), (4.23), and (4.24) provide a recurrence formula which can be employed to evaluate the optimal rule, $\hat{u} = \{\hat{u}_0, \hat{u}_1, \ldots, \hat{u}_N\}$.

The second example to be considered is much more interesting from the conceptual point of view. In this system there is a random parameter for which the complete statistical characterization is not known. Thus, the control element must "learn" about this parameter as the process evolves. The equation which describes the system is the scalar difference equation:

$$\begin{aligned} x_{j+1} &= \xi_j x_j + v_j, \qquad 0 \leqslant j \leqslant N, \\ x_1 &= x(1), \\ \tilde{x}_j &\equiv 0. \end{aligned} \tag{4.25}$$

The observable information vector is given by

$$z_j = \begin{bmatrix} x^j \\ v^{j-1} \end{bmatrix}.$$

The object of the control policy is to minimize the expected value of a measure of the final value of the state variable.

$$H(\bar{u}, \theta_0^*) = E\{x_N{}^2\}.$$

It will be assumed that ξ^N is a sequence of independent random variables with probability density

$$p(\xi_j \mid \theta, \xi^{j-1}) = \frac{1}{\sqrt{\pi}} \exp\{-(\xi_j - \theta)^2\}.$$

Here θ plays the role of the unknown parameter for the system. We assume Θ to be the real line. Note the essential difference between this example and the one preceding. If Θ contained only one point, $\tilde{\theta}$, this system would be contained in the set of systems described by Eq. (4.18). For every different $\tilde{\theta}$, we would arrive at a different optimal control policy. Thus, the problem of finding an optimal policy does not have a solution in the same sense it had in the first example. As discussed earlier, if there exists some *a priori* information on θ, a Bayes policy would seem appropriate. For this example, however, it will be assumed that no such *a priori* information exists, and a minimax policy is sought. The approach suggested in Theorem 3.9 will be pursued.

To apply this theory, the form of the Bayes rules for various $\theta_\epsilon^* \in \Theta^*$ must be examined. The set of all probability distributions over the real line is clearly a very large set. If one is fortunate, the sequence of $\theta_\epsilon^* \in \Theta^*$ which are called for by Definition 3.1 can be chosen from a small subset of Θ^*. With this in mind, let us investigate the Bayes policies for $\theta_0^* = \mathrm{Nor}(\mu, \sigma^2)$; that is,

$$p_0(\theta) = \frac{1}{\sqrt{2\pi}\sigma} \exp\left\{-\frac{(\theta - \mu)^2}{2\sigma^2}\right\}.$$

It is shown in Appendix A that a Bayes policy with respect to θ_0^* is given by

$$\hat{u}_j = \left[-\frac{2a_{3,j}\left(2\sum_{i=0}^{j-1} \frac{x_{i+1} - v_i}{x_i} - \frac{\mu}{2\sigma^2}\right)}{a_{1,j}} + \frac{a_{2,j}\left(\sum_{i=0}^{j-1} \frac{x_{j+1} - v_i}{x_i} - \frac{\mu}{2\sigma^2}\right)}{a_{1,j}}\right] x_j, \quad 1 \leqslant j \leqslant N. \tag{4.26}$$

One method of finding the minimax control policy involves finding an equalizer rule. An obvious guess at an equalizer would be simply to use the minimum-variance unbiased estimate for θ in the formula for the optimal control policy where θ is known. Denote this policy by $\bar{\omega}$. From Eq. (4.25) it is clear that the optimal control rule if θ is known is given by

$$\bar{u}_j = -\theta x_j , \qquad 1 \leqslant j \leqslant N.$$

Therefore,

$$\bar{\omega}_j = -\left\{\frac{1}{j}\sum_{i=0}^{j-1}\frac{x_{i+1}-v_i}{x_i}\right\} x_j , \qquad 1 \leqslant j \leqslant N.$$

From Eq. (4.26),

$$\hat{u}_j \Big|_{\mu=0} = -\frac{4a_{3,j}-a_{2,j}}{a_{1,j}}\sum_{i=0}^{j-1}\frac{x_{i+1}-v_i}{x_i} x_j .$$

From the results presented in Appendix B, it is apparent that

$$\lim_{\sigma\to\infty} \hat{u}_j \Big|_{\mu=0} = -\frac{[4/2(j+1)]-[1/(j+1)]}{j/(j+1)}\sum_{i=0}^{j-1}\frac{x_{i+1}-v_i}{x_i} x_j$$

$$= -\frac{1}{j}\sum_{i=0}^{j-1}\frac{x_{i+1}-v_i}{x_i} x_j , \qquad j = 1, \ldots, N.$$

Consequently,

$$\lim_{\sigma^2\to\infty} \hat{u} = \bar{\omega}.$$

This, in itself, is not sufficient to prove that $\bar{\omega}$ is extended Bayes because we must prove

$$\lim_{\sigma^2\to\infty} H(\hat{u}, \theta_0{}^*(\sigma^2)) = \lim_{\sigma^2\to\infty} H(\bar{\omega}, \theta_0{}^*(\sigma^2)).$$

The notation $\theta_0{}^*(\sigma^2)$ has been used to indicate the dependence of the *a priori* distribution for θ on the parameter σ^2. Equation (A.18) shows that

$$\lim_{\sigma^2\to\infty} H(\hat{u}, \theta_0{}^*(\sigma^2)) = N_1 x(1)^2 \tag{4.27}$$

where N_1 is a uniformly bounded function of σ^2 for $\sigma^2 \in (0, \infty)$. The criterion function is continuous in v, and therefore,

$$\lim_{\sigma^2 \to \infty} H(\bar{\omega}, \theta_0^*(\sigma^2)) = N_1 x(1)^2. \tag{4.28}$$

Equations (4.27) and (4.28) prove that $\bar{\omega}$ is an extended Bayes control rule. We must now show that it is an equalizer. Before treating this question in detail, let us consider the following heuristic argument. Because of the manner in which the problem is formulated, ρ_1 provides a measure of the expected cost of the process conditioned on x_1, x_0, and v_0. In general, one might expect that ρ_1 would be implicitly dependent on ξ_0, and thus, explicitly on $(x_1 - v_0)/x_0$ since ξ_0 provides some indication of the true value of θ. Instead, as the *a priori* information approaches the uniform "distribution" over the real line, ρ_1 becomes independent of ξ_0. Consequently, for every ξ_0, ρ_1 is the same, and we might begin to suspect that the Bayes cost of $\hat{u}$ is becoming less dependent on the true value of θ as $\sigma^2 \to \infty$.

The simplest way to prove that $\bar{\omega}$ is an equalizer rule is to argue as follows.

$$h(x, \bar{\omega}, \tilde{x}) = \left[\prod_{i=1}^{N-1} \left(\xi_i - \frac{1}{i}\sum_{i=0}^{i-1} \xi_j\right) x(1)\right]^2.$$

Therefore,

$$H(\bar{\omega}, \theta) = x(1)^2 E\left\{\prod_{i=1}^{N-1} \left(\xi_i - \frac{1}{i}\sum_{j=0}^{i-1} \xi_j\right)^2\right\}.$$

It is easy to see that the $(\xi_i - (1/i) \sum_{j=0}^{i-1} \xi_j)$ are a sequence of independent random variables with zero mean and variance equal to $\frac{1}{2}(1 + (1/i))$. Therefore,

$$H(\bar{\omega}, \theta) = \left(\frac{1}{2}\right)^{N-1} x(1)^2 \prod_{i=1}^{N-1} \left(1 + \frac{1}{i}\right)$$

for all $\theta \in \Theta$, and consequently, $\bar{\omega} \in \Gamma$ is a minimax control policy.

6. Conclusions

Since such a nice solution was obtained in the second example, the reader might wonder what would have happened if the initial condition was placed on x_0 rather than x_1. For this problem the solution is quite simple. All $\bar{u} \in \Gamma$ are minimax. The truth of this assertion follows from the fact that even if we have a good estimate of θ, the expected cost of the process is proportional to x_1^2. If ξ_0 is not measured before the initiation of control, nature is permitted sufficient freedom to make $E\{x_1^2\} = \infty$ for all v_0.

It is clear that by describing the motion of the control process with a set of difference equations we have introduced an important mathematical restriction on the class of problems which can be treated. In most physical systems, however, this does not seem to be an unnatural method of description. In particular, if the loop contains inertial elements and if the control energy is bounded, it is intuitively clear that a discrete time model of the process will be adequate if the time increment is chosen appropriately. In the same way, if the control policy approaches some limiting form as $N \to \infty$, the results of this technique may be suitable for optimization over an infinite period.

Discussion

SECTIONS 2–4. The functional equation (4.16) was derived by Fel'dbaum in the series of papers [1–4].

SECTION 5. The first example was originally solved using dynamic programming in Gunckel and Franklin [5]. Other examples of the use of the dual control formalism appear in Fel'dbaum [6], Zhigulev [7], and Maslov [8]. Fel'dbaum [9] presents a lucid description of dual control theory and provides several examples.

Bibliography

1. A. A. Fel'dbaum, "Dual Control Theory 1," *Automation and Remote Control*, Vol. 21, No. 9, pp. 874–880 (September 1960).
2. A. A. Fel'dbaum, "Dual Control Theory 2," *Automation and Remote Control*, Vol. 21, No. 11, pp. 1033–1039 (November 1960).
3. A. A. Fel'dbaum, "Dual Control Theory 3," *Automation and Remote Control*, Vol. 22, No. 1, pp. 1–12 (January 1961).
4. A. A. Fel'dbaum, "Dual Control Theory 4," *Automation and Remote Control*, Vol. 22, No. 2, pp. 109–121 (February 1961).

5. T. L. Gunckel and G. F. Franklin, "A General Solution for Linear Sampled-Data Control," *ASME Journal of Basic Engineering*, Vol. 85, pp. 197–203 (June 1963).
6. A. A. Fel'dbaum, "On the Optimal Control of Markov Objects," *Automation and Remote Control*, Vol. 23, No. 8, pp. 927–941 (August 1962).
7. Z. N. Zhigulev, "Synthesis of a Certain Class of Optimal Systems," *Automation and Remote Control*, Vol. 23, No. 11, pp. 1344–1351 (November 1962).
8. E. P. Maslov, "Application of the Theory of Statistical Decisions to the Estimation of Object Parameters," *Automation and Remote Control*, Vol. 24, No. 10, pp. 1214–1226 (October 1963).
9. A. A. Fel'dbaum, *Optimal Control Systems,* Academic Press, New York, 1966, Chapter 6.

CHAPTER 5

Control of Linear Systems with a Markov Property

1. Introduction

In some control system applications the engineer is faced with the problem of controlling a plant which has a random characteristic. This randomness may be occasioned by noise in a measurement channel or perhaps through variation in the system environment with resulting change in system parameters. Recently, interest has developed in the problem of optimal control of such plants. The basic method of solution involves using the formalism of dynamic programming to derive a recurrence formula or partial differential equation which the optimal control policy must satisfy. The class of systems most amenable to this type of analysis is the usual "linear plant, quadratic criterion" class, but, at least in principle, the range of problems could be extended.

One property which characterizes this group of problems is the fact that the criterion of performance induces a total ordering on the set of allowable control rules. This follows from the fact that the behavior of each element in the system is known sufficiently well to account for its effect on the performance index. Since it will seldom be the case that the engineer will have enough *a priori* knowledge to determine the exact joint probability distribution of the random elements of the system, it is of interest to investigate the control of such a system in the presence of uncertainty about the values of certain parameters.

In Chapter 4 we derived a recurrence formula which the Bayes control policy with respect to a given *a priori* distribution for θ must satisfy. The example of the design of an adaptive control system which was presented in that chapter involved the control of a scalar process in which the disturbance component, ξ^N, was a sequence of random numbers which were independent from one time increment to the next. Let us now generalize this adaptive control problem. Assume that the object to be controlled is described by a linear vector difference equation. The object is subject to an additive disturbance with known statistical properties at the input, and the parameters of the difference equations are functions of a second random process. It is this second stochastic process which introduces the adaptive nature of the control problem because it is assumed to be a discrete parameter Markov process with an unknown statistical parameter, θ. The control system designer must choose a control sequence $\bar{v} \in \Gamma$ so that the output of the system follows a random input, $\tilde{x}^N$, in such a way as to minimize some criterion of performance.

Before the problem can be discussed in a meaningful fashion, we must specify the quantity of *a priori* knowledge that the control system designer possesses at the beginning of the process. It will be assumed that the engineer knows that θ is a real number, but has no precise information beyond this. He might express his intuitive feeling about θ by saying that all real values for θ appear equally likely. In addition to this *a priori* probability information on θ, it might happen that the designer has some knowledge of past operation of the system; that is, several increments of time may have already passed before the initiation of control action. The input and output records of the plant for these time increments provide information about the true value of θ.

The problem we propose to analyze is, therefore, a discrete time, adaptive version of the stochastic system problems mentioned earlier. We will analyze the effect of both additive disturbances and plant variations, and we will require the plant to follow a random input. In Section 2, these ideas will be made more precise by defining the control problem in more detail. A particular sequence of Bayes control policies is derived in Section 3 and the properties of the limit of this sequence are explored in Section 4. In the last part of the chapter a class of systems for which this limiting policy is minimax is investigated and an example is studied at length.

2. Mathematical Formulation

The fixed element of the control system will be described by the vector difference equation

$$x_{j+1} = \phi_j(\xi_j)x_j + \Delta_j(\xi_j)v_j + \Theta_j(\xi_j)\eta_j, \qquad 0 \leqslant j \leqslant N, \qquad x_q = x(q), \tag{5.1}$$

where

x_j = the n-dimensional state vector at time $t = j\Delta$; Δ is the unit increment of time;

v_j = the scalar control action at $t = j\Delta$;

η_j, ξ_j = the scalar random disturbance at $t = j\Delta$;

$x(q)$ = the n-dimensional initial condition vector; q is an integer in the interval $[0, N]$.

The set of allowable control actions V_j will be taken to be E_1. There are two random disturbances which act on the system. The first is an additive scalar disturbance which has the effect of noise in the channel transmitting the control action, v_j. This term, η^N, is a sequence of independent, identically distributed, random variables with probability density function $p(\eta)$. We will assume that

$$\begin{aligned} E\{\eta_i\} &= 0, & 0 \leqslant i \leqslant N, \\ E\{\eta_i\eta_j\} &= \sigma_\lambda^2 < \infty, & i = j = 0, ..., N, \\ &= 0, & i \neq j. \end{aligned} \tag{5.2}$$

The second random disturbance, ξ^N, creates a different effect in the system than the sequence η^N did. This disturbance causes a change in the transition properties of the system. Thus, the plant is not only time variable in a deterministic sense, but it is also stochastic. For convenience in notation we will usually suppress the explicit dependence of $\phi_j(\xi_j)$, $\Delta_j(\xi_j)$, and $\Theta_j(\xi_j)$ on the random variable ξ_j. It will be assumed, however, that such a dependence exists unless otherwise stated. We will assume ξ^N to be a scalar, discrete parameter Wiener process described by a conditional probability density function of the form

$$p(\xi_i \mid \xi^{i-1}, \theta) = \frac{1}{\sqrt{2\pi}\sigma} \exp\left\{-\frac{(\xi_i - \xi_{i-1} - \theta)^2}{2\sigma^2}\right\}. \tag{5.3}$$

The scalar θ constitutes the essential unknown quantity which parameterizes the index of performance. It is known that $\theta \in \Theta$ where $\Theta = \{\theta \mid -\infty < \theta < \infty\}$.

Let us now specify the *a priori* knowledge about the system which the control system designer has at his disposal at the time the control process begins. It will be assumed that Eq. (5.1) and Θ are known, and further that the first q stages of the process have already taken place before optimal control is initiated. Clearly, as q becomes larger more information on system performance is available during the initial stages of control.

With the plant at least partially described, one can proceed to consider the function which the plant is to perform. Suppose that the control system is to be designed in such a way that it will cause some linear scalar function of the plant state vector to track a random input $\tilde{x}_j$ described by the relation

$$p(\tilde{x}_i \mid \tilde{x}^{i-1}) = \frac{1}{\sqrt{2\pi}\sigma_w} \exp\left\{-\frac{(\tilde{x}_i - \tilde{x}_{i-1})^2}{2\sigma_w^2}\right\}. \tag{5.4}$$

The input is a scalar Wiener process with Gaussian increments. The quality of the compensation device will be measured by the criterion functional:

$$h(\tilde{x}^N, x^N, v^N) = \sum_{i=q}^{N} (\tilde{x}_i - Hx_i)^2 + \beta_i v_i^2, \qquad \beta_i \geqslant 0. \tag{5.5}$$

The final bit of information which the engineer must specify before this control problem can be attacked in a meaningful fashion is the quantity of data that the controller may acquire as the process unfolds in time. Since a discrete time process is being considered, these data take the form of a vector composed of the measured system variables. If this observation vector is called z_j, then it will be assumed that

$$z_j = \begin{bmatrix} \tilde{x}_j \\ x_j \\ \xi_{j-1} \\ v_{j-1} \\ z_{j-1} \end{bmatrix}.$$

3. Evaluation of $\overline{u(\infty)}$

Since this is an adaptive problem, the criterion of performance does not induce a total ordering of the control policies. The control system designer must, therefore, choose an appropriate auxiliary criterion to provide a linear ordering of Γ^*. Since no *a priori* $\theta_0^* \in \Theta^*$ was given in the problem formulation, a max-cost ordering might seem desirable in this situation. For the general system defined by Eq. (5.1) the minimax control policy would be very difficult to determine since a least favorable distribution, if such exists, will depend on the particular form of the ϕ_j, Δ_j, and Θ_j. Let us disregard for the time being the max-cost ordering and assume that the control system designer expressed his initial ignorance of the true value of θ by the vague feeling that all real values of θ are equally likely. The uniform "distribution" on the real line is not a probability distribution so this *a priori* knowledge cannot be readily expressed as an element $\theta^* \in \Theta^*$.

Let us, therefore, reformulate the problem as follows: Define $\overline{u(n)}$ to be a Bayes control policy with respect to $\theta^*_{n\sigma^2} = \text{Nor}(0, n\sigma^2)$. Now $\theta^*_{n\sigma^2} \in \Theta^*$ for all $n \geqslant 0$ and if $\overline{u(n)}$ exists then $\overline{u(n)} \in \Gamma$. It is clear that as n increases the probability density function associated with $\theta^*_{n\sigma^2}$ approaches the *a priori* "distribution" over bounded subsets of Θ. One is, therefore, tempted to define $\lim_{n\to\infty} \overline{u(n)} = \overline{u(\infty)}$ to be the optimal control policy.

There are, to be sure, difficulties attendant on such a definition. There are the problems of existence of the $\overline{u(n)}$ and $\overline{u(\infty)}$. There is another problem which is slightly more subtle. Since the system state is continuous in $\bar{u}$, and since the criterion of performance is continuous in $\bar{u}$ and x^N, one would certainly expect that $H(\overline{u(n)}, \theta^*_{n\sigma^2})$ is some finite number for each $n \geqslant 0$. It seems reasonable to suppose that $H(\overline{u(n)}, \theta^*_{n\sigma^2})$ is an increasing function of n since as n increases, the *a priori* information seems less precise. Unfortunately, if $\lim_{n\to\infty} H(\overline{u(n)}, \theta^*_{n\sigma^2}) = \infty$, the problem formulation has little practical meaning because in this case $\lim_{n\to\infty} H(\bar{u}, \theta^*_{n\sigma^2}) = \infty$ for all $\bar{u} \in \Gamma$. With these difficulties in mind let us proceed to evaluate $\overline{u(n)}$. The specific optimality properties of $\overline{u(\infty)}$ will be investigated in the next section.

In principle at least, application of Eqs. (4.16) and (4.17) permits the solution of this problem to be obtained for any *a priori* distribution. For the linear system described by Eq. (5.1) if we suppress the obvious factors due to the initial conditions on ξ^N and $\tilde{x}^N$, the following equation for α_j results:

$$\alpha_j = \int \frac{W_j \prod_{i=0}^{j} \delta_{x_i} [\prod_{i=1}^{j-1} p(\xi_i \mid \xi_{i-1}, \theta)]^2 \prod_{i=1}^{j} p(\tilde{x}_i \mid \tilde{x}_{i-1}) \prod_{i=0}^{j-1} p(\eta_i) p_0(\theta)}{\int \prod_{i=1}^{j-1} p(\xi_i \mid \xi_{i-1}, \theta) p_0(\theta)\, d\Omega(\theta)} \times d\Omega(\theta, \eta^{j-1}) \tag{5.6}$$

where

$$\delta_{x_i} = \delta(x_i - \phi_{i-1} x_{i-1} - \Delta_{i-1} v_{i-1} - \Theta_{i-1} \eta_{i-1}).$$

In Appendix C it is shown that

$$\int \frac{[\prod_{j=1}^{i-1} p(\xi_j \mid \xi_{j-1}, \theta)]^2 \, p_0(\theta)}{\int \prod_{j=1}^{i-1} p(\xi_j \mid \xi_{j-1}, \gamma) p_0(\gamma) d\Omega(\gamma)} d\Omega(\theta) = \frac{1}{\sqrt{2}} \left(\frac{1}{\sqrt{2n\sigma}}\right)^{i-1} \exp\{a_i\} + O\left(\frac{1}{\sqrt{n}}\right) \tag{5.7}$$

where

$$a_{1,i} = \frac{1}{2\sigma^2} \sum_{j=1}^{i-1} (\xi_j - \xi_{j-1}),$$

$$a_{2,i} = \frac{1}{2\sigma^2} \sum_{j=1}^{i-1} (\xi_j - \xi_{j-1})^2,$$

$$a_i = -a_{2,i} + \frac{2\sigma^2}{i-1} a_{1,i}^2 .$$

We will denote the fact that α_j is a function of the *a priori* distribution $\theta^*_{n\sigma^2}$ by $\alpha_j(n)$. Then it follows that

$$\alpha_j(n) = \int [(\tilde{x}_j - Hx_j)^2 + \beta_j v_j^2] \prod_{i=0}^{j} \delta_{x_i} \left[\left(\frac{1}{\sqrt{2\pi\sigma_w}}\right)^j \exp\left\{-\frac{1}{2\sigma_w^2} \sum_{i=1}^{j} (\tilde{x}_i - \tilde{x}_{i-1})^2\right\}\right]$$
$$\times \left[\prod_{i=0}^{j-1} p(\eta_i)\right] \left[\left(\frac{1}{\sqrt{2\pi\sigma}}\right)^{j-1} \frac{1}{\sqrt{2}} \exp\{a_j\} + O\left(\frac{1}{\sqrt{n}}\right)\right] d\Omega(\eta^{j-1}). \tag{5.8}$$

From Eq. (4.16) it is evident that we must first evaluate ρ_N.

$$\rho_N = \min_{\bar{u}_N} \alpha_N .$$

The minimum of $\alpha_N(n)$ occurs when $\bar{u}_N \equiv 0$. Consequently,

$$\rho_N(n) = \int [(\tilde{x}_N - Hx_N)^2] \prod_{i=0}^{N} \delta_{x_i} \left[\left(\frac{1}{\sqrt{2\pi}\sigma_w} \right)^N \exp \left\{ - \frac{1}{2\sigma_w{}^2} \sum_{i=1}^{N} (\tilde{x}_i - \tilde{x}_{i-1})^2 \right\} \right]$$

$$\times \left[\prod_{i=0}^{N-1} p(\eta_i) \right] \left[\left(\frac{1}{\sqrt{2\pi}\sigma} \right)^{N-1} \frac{1}{\sqrt{2}} \exp\{a_N\} + O\left(\frac{1}{\sqrt{n}} \right) \right] d\Omega(\eta^{N-1}). \quad (5.9)$$

In Appendix D it is shown that the optimal control at time $t = (N-1)\Delta$ is given by the relation

$$\overline{u(n)}_{N-1} = \frac{\overline{H\Delta_{N-1}}\, \tilde{x}_{N-1} - \overline{H\Delta_{N-1} H\phi_{N-1}}\, x_{N-1}}{(H\Delta_{N-1})^2 + \sqrt{(N-2)/N}\, \beta_{N-1}} + O\left(\frac{1}{\sqrt{n}} \right),$$

where we have used the following notation. If $H_{N-j-1}(\xi_{N-j-1})$ is some function of ξ_{N-j-1} for which the following integral exists, then

$$\sqrt{\frac{N-j-2}{2\pi\sigma^2(N-j-1)}} \int_{-\infty}^{\infty} H_{N-j-1}(\xi_{N-j-1})$$

$$\times \exp \left\{ - \frac{N-j-2}{2\sigma^2(N-j-1)} \left(\xi_{N-j-1} - \xi_{N-j-2} - \frac{2\sigma^2}{N-j-2}\, a_{1,N-j-1} \right)^2 \right\} d\xi_{N-j-1}$$

$$= \bar{H}_{N-j-1} .$$

A measure of the Bayes cost for the last two stages of the process is given by

$$\rho_{N-1}(n) = K_{N-1} \int [L_{N-1}(\xi, \eta) + x_{N-1}^T P_{N-1} x_{N-1} + R_{N-1} \tilde{x}_{N-1}^2$$

$$+ Q_{N-1} x_{N-1} \tilde{x}_{N-1} + A_{N-1}(\tilde{x}_{N-1} - Hx_{N-1})^2] \quad (5.10)$$

$$\times \prod_{i=0}^{N-1} \delta x_i \left[\left(\frac{1}{\sqrt{2\pi}\sigma_w} \right)^{N-1} \exp \left\{ - \frac{1}{2\sigma_w{}^2} \sum_{i=1}^{N-1} (\tilde{x}_i - \tilde{x}_{i-1})^2 \right\} \right]$$

$$\times \prod_{i=0}^{N-2} p(\eta_i) \left[\left(\frac{1}{\sqrt{2\pi}\sigma} \right)^{N-2} \exp\{a_{N-1}\} + O\left(\frac{1}{\sqrt{n}} \right) \right] d\Omega(\eta^{N-2}),$$

where

$$K_{N-1} = \sqrt{\frac{N}{2(N-2)}},$$

$$A_{N-1} = \sqrt{\frac{N-2}{N}},$$

$$P_{N-1} = \overline{\phi_{N-1}^T H^T H \phi_{N-1}} + \frac{\overline{(\phi_{N-1}^T H^T \Delta_{N-1}^T H^T)}\ \overline{(H\Delta_{N-1} H\phi_{N-1})}}{M_{N-1}},$$

$$Q_{N-1} = -2\overline{H\phi_{N-1}} - 2\frac{\overline{H\Delta_{N-1}}\ \overline{H\Delta_{N-1}H\phi_{N-1}}}{M_{N-1}}, \tag{5.11}$$

$$R_{N-1} = 1 + \frac{\overline{(H\Delta_{N-1})^2}}{M_{N-1}},$$

$$M_{N-1} = \overline{(H\Delta_{N-1})^2} + \sqrt{\frac{N-2}{N}}\,\beta_{N-1},$$

$$L_{N-1} = \sigma_w^2 + \overline{(H\Theta)^2}\sigma_\lambda^2.$$

By an induction argument, it is shown in Appendix E that

$$\begin{aligned}
\overline{u(n)}_{N-j-1} &= -\Bigg(x_{N-j-1}^T\,\overline{\Phi_{N-j-1}^T P_{N-j}\Delta_{N-j-1}} - \sqrt{\frac{N-j-1}{N}}\,\overline{H\Delta_{N-j-1}}\,\tilde{x}_{N-j-1} \\
&\quad + \sqrt{\frac{N-j-1}{N}}\,\overline{H\Delta_{N-j-1}H\Phi_{N-j-1}}\,x_{N-j-1} \\
&\quad + \frac{1}{2}\overline{Q_{N-j}\Delta_{N-j-1}}\,\tilde{x}_{N-j-1}\Bigg) M_{N-j-1}^{-1} \\
&\quad + O\left(\frac{1}{\sqrt{n}}\right), \qquad q \leqslant N-j-1 < N, \\
&= 0, \qquad N-j-1 = N,
\end{aligned} \tag{5.12}$$

and

$$\begin{aligned}
\rho(n)_{N-j-1} &= \sqrt{\frac{N}{2(N-j-2)}} \int \Big\{ L_{N-j-1}(\xi, \eta) \\
&\quad + x_{N-j-1}^T P_{N-j-1} x_{N-j-1} + R_{N-j-1}\tilde{x}_{N-j-1}^2
\end{aligned}$$

$$+ Q_{N-j-1}x_{N-j-1}\tilde{x}_{N-j-1} + \sqrt{\frac{N-j-2}{N}}\,(\tilde{x}_{N-j-1} - Hx_{N-j-1})^2\Big\}$$

$$\times \prod_{i=0}^{N-j-1} \delta_{x_i} \prod_{i=0}^{N-j-2} p(\eta_i) \prod_{i=0}^{N-j-1} p(\tilde{x}_i \mid \tilde{x}_{i-1})$$

$$\times \left[\left(\frac{1}{\sqrt{2\pi\sigma}}\right)^{N-j-2} \exp\{a_{N-j-1}\} + O\left(\frac{1}{\sqrt{n}}\right)\right] d\Omega(\eta^{N-j-2}). \qquad (5.13)$$

A recurrence formula for the parameters of Eqs. (5.12) and (5.13) are given in Appendix E.

From Eqs. (5.12) and (5.13) the explicit expression for $\overline{u(\infty)}$ and $\lim_{n\to\infty} H(\overline{u(n)}, \theta^*_{n\sigma^2})$ can be written directly:

$$\begin{aligned}\overline{u(\infty)}_j &= \lim_{n\to\infty} \overline{u(n)}_j \\ &= -\left[x_j^T\,\overline{\phi_j^T P_{j+1} \Delta_j} - \sqrt{\frac{j}{N}}\,\overline{H\Delta_j}\tilde{x}_j + \sqrt{\frac{j}{N}}\,\overline{H\Delta_j H\phi_j}x_j \right. \\ &\qquad \left. + \frac{1}{2}\overline{Q_{j+1}\Delta_j}\tilde{x}_j\right] M_j^{-1}, \qquad q \leqslant j < N, \\ &= 0, \qquad\qquad\qquad\qquad j = N,\end{aligned} \qquad (5.14)$$

and

$$\begin{aligned}\lim_{n\to\infty} H(\overline{u(n)}, \theta^*_{n\sigma^2}) &= \lim_{n\to\infty} \int \rho_q(n) p(\tilde{x}^q, \xi^{q-1})\, d\Omega(\tilde{x}^q, \xi^{q-1}) \\ &= \sqrt{\frac{N}{2(q-1)}} \int \Big\{ L_q(\xi, \eta) + x_q^T P_q x_q + R_q \tilde{x}_q^2 + Q_q x_q \tilde{x}_q \\ &\qquad + \sqrt{\frac{q-1}{N}}\,(\tilde{x}_q - Hx_q)^2 \Big\} \prod_{i=1}^{q} p(\tilde{x}_i \mid \tilde{x}_{i-1}) \\ &\qquad \times \prod_{i=0}^{q-1} p(\eta_i) \left[\left(\frac{1}{\sqrt{2\pi\sigma}}\right)^{q-1} \exp\{a_q\}\right] \\ &\qquad \times p(\tilde{x}_0, \xi_0)\, d\Omega(\eta^{q-1}, \tilde{x}^q, \xi^{q-1}).\end{aligned} \qquad (5.15)$$

4. Properties of $\overline{u(\infty)}$

Equation (5.12) provides us with an explicit relation for a Bayes control policy with respect to $\theta^*_{n\sigma^2}$ and Eq. (5.14) gives $\overline{u(\infty)}$. From the discussion at the beginning of Section 3 it is apparent that $H(\overline{u(n)}, \theta^*_{n\sigma^2})$ must be uniformly bounded in order that the problem formulation presented here be meaningful. From Eq. (5.15) we see that a necessary and sufficient condition that $H(\overline{u(n)}, \theta^*_{n\sigma^2})$ be uniformly bounded for all initial values of the system state is

$$\begin{aligned} \| P_q \| &< \infty, \\ \| Q_q \| &< \infty, \\ \| R_q \| &< \infty, \\ \| L_q \| &< \infty, \end{aligned} \tag{5.16}$$

and

$$q \geqslant 2.$$

The restrictions on the boundedness of the matrices seems to be a reasonable constraint in any physical control system design situation, but the basis for the restriction on q may not be intuitively clear. This apparent anomaly results from the fact that the compensation element must acquire some information on the true value of θ before satisfactory system performance can be obtained. Suppose, for example, that $q = 0$ in Eq. (5.1). Then Eq. (5.15) indicates that every control policy in Γ^* is minimax. In a situation such as posed in this chapter in which the engineer is called upon to synthesize a compensation element for a fixed plant in the presence of uncertainty about the values of certain parameters, the engineer will seek what we have labeled a "reasonable" control rule; that is, the control rule should incorporate whatever prior knowledge the designer has at his disposal into a form which appears to be adequate to cause the controlled object to perform its specified function. The max-cost ordering is simply one tool which can be used to derive a control policy which is "reasonable" in this sense. For the case where $q = 0$, the ordering induced by the max-cost makes every control strategy equivalent, and thus, does not provide a "reasonable" control rule. But max-cost is not inviolate, and it is certainly within the domain of the engineer to modify the form of the max-cost if this procedure will enable him to find a satisfactory compensation. In the problem considered here, a control engineer might determine v_0 through v_{q-1} by evaluating the first q elements of the Bayes control with respect to some $\theta^* \in \Theta^*$. Since the unbounded value of $\lim_{n\to\infty} H(\bar{u}, \theta)^*_{n\sigma^2}$ for this choice of $\bar{u}$

could be the result of simplifications in the model of the physical process, the engineer might find the resulting control rule completely satisfactory. In what follows we will assume that $q \geqslant 2$ and that the matrix inequalities of Eq. (5.16) are satisfied.

Now that the explicit form of $\overline{u(n)}$ and $\overline{u(\infty)}$ has been displayed in Eqs. (5.12) and (5.14), we can return to the question of the specific optimality properties of $\overline{u(\infty)}$. Since $\overline{u(\infty)}$ is a limit of Bayes policies, we would intuitively expect $\overline{u(\infty)}$ to be an extended Bayes control policy. Unfortunately, this is not always the case. A restriction must be placed on how the cost of the control process grows with n. For our purposes the restriction provided by condition (3) of Theorem 5.1 is in the most desirable form. This condition is essentially a continuity requirement on the expected cost of the remaining stages of the process. Since a measure of this expected cost must be computed at every stage of the control process in order to compute $\overline{u(\infty)}$, no additional computational labor is necessary to verify condition (3) in an actual design problem.

Theorem 5.1. *Let the control problem satisfy the following conditions.*

(1) *System equation:* $x_{j+1} = f_j(x_j, v_j, \xi_j)$, $0 \leqslant j \leqslant N-1$.

(2) *Criterion function:*

$$H(\bar{v}, \theta^*) = \sum_{i=q}^{N} R_i(\bar{v}, \theta^*).$$

(3) f_j *and* R_j *are such that if* $\bar{v} \in \Gamma$ *and* $\bar{w} \in \Gamma$ *and if*

$$\begin{aligned} \bar{v}_j - \bar{w}_j &= 0, & 0 \leqslant j < k, \quad k < j \leqslant N, \\ &= \bar{v}_k - \bar{w}_k, & j = k, \end{aligned}$$

then for every $\epsilon > 0$ *there exists* $\delta > 0$ *such that if* $\| \bar{v}_k - \bar{w}_k \| < \delta$,

$$\left| \sum_{i=k}^{N} R_i(\bar{v}, \theta^*_{n\sigma^2}) - \sum_{i=k}^{N} R_i(\bar{w}, \theta^*_{n\sigma^2}) \right| < \epsilon,$$

where $\theta^*_{n\sigma^2} = \mathrm{Nor}(0, n\sigma^2)$ *and* δ *is independent of* n.

If $\overline{u(n)} \in \Gamma$ *is a Bayes control policy with respect to* $\theta^*_{n\sigma^2}$, *and if* $\lim_{n\to\infty} \overline{u(n)} = \overline{u(\infty)} \in \Gamma$, *then* $\overline{u(\infty)}$ *is an extended Bayes control policy.*

Proof. Following our usual notation, if $\overline{u(n)} \in \Gamma$, then $\overline{u(n)}_j$ is the value of $\overline{u(n)}$ when $t = j\Delta$. Define the following control policy:

$$\begin{aligned} \overline{t_k(n)} &= \overline{u(n)}_j\,, & 0 \leqslant j < k, \\ &= \overline{u(\infty)}_j\,, & k \leqslant j \leqslant N. \end{aligned}$$

By definition

$$H(\overline{t_k(n)}, \theta^*_{n\sigma^2}) = \sum_{i=q}^{N} R_i(\overline{t_k(n)}, \theta^*_{n\sigma^2}).$$

Consequently

$$H(\overline{t_N(n)}, \theta^*_{n\sigma^2}) - H(\overline{u(n)}, \theta^*_{n\sigma^2}) = R_N(\overline{t_N(n)}, \theta^*_{n\sigma^2}) - R_N(\overline{u(n)}, \theta^*_{n\sigma^2}).$$

By hypothesis, there exists a M_N such that if $n > M_N$,

$$| R_N(\overline{t_N(n)}, \theta^*_{n\sigma^2}) - R_N(\overline{u(n)}, \theta^*_{n\sigma^2})| < \frac{\epsilon}{N}\,.$$

Thus, if $n > M_N$,

$$| H(\overline{t_N(n)}, \theta^*_{n\sigma^2}) - H(\overline{u(n)}, \theta^*_{n\sigma^2})| < \frac{\epsilon}{N}\,.$$

Let us assume that

$$| H(\overline{t_{N-j+1}(n)}, \theta^*_{n\sigma^2}) - H(\overline{u(n)}, \theta^*_{n\sigma^2})| < \frac{j\epsilon}{N}$$

whenever $n > M_{N-j+1}$. We can write

$$\begin{aligned} H(\overline{t_{N-j}(n)}, \theta^*_{n\sigma^2}) - H(\overline{u(n)}, \theta^*_{n\sigma^2}) &= H(\overline{t_{N-j+1}(n)}, \theta^*_{n\sigma^2}) - H(\overline{u(n)}, \theta^*_{n\sigma^2}) \\ &\quad + H(\overline{t_{N-j}(n)}\theta^*_{n\sigma^2}) - H(\overline{t_{N-j+1}(n)}, \theta^*_{n\sigma^2}). \end{aligned}$$

Let

$$| H(\overline{t_{N-j}(n)}, \theta^*_{n\sigma^2}) - H(\overline{t_{N-j+1}(n)}, \theta^*_{n\sigma^2})^* | < \frac{\epsilon}{N}$$

whenever $n > R$. Then,

$$| H(\overline{t_{N-j}(n)}, \theta^*_{n\sigma^2}) - H(\overline{u(n)}, \theta^*_{n\sigma^2})| < \frac{j+1}{N}\,\epsilon$$

whenever $n > M_{N-j} = \max\{M_{N-j+1}, R\}$. By induction, there exists an M_q such that if $n > M_q$

$$|H(\overline{u(\infty)}, \theta^*_{n\sigma^2}) - H(\overline{u(n)}, \theta^*_{n\sigma^2})| < \epsilon.$$

Therefore, $\overline{u(\infty)}$ is an extended Bayes control policy. ▼

Theorem 5.1 provides a general framework for determining if a particular limit of Bayes policies is extended Bayes. These conditions, however, do not place explicit restrictions on the form of ϕ_j, Δ_j, and Θ_j. If attention is restricted to linear systems with a quadratic criterion of performance, the following result is obtained.

Theorem 5.2. *If* $\lim_{n\to\infty} H(\overline{u(n)}, \theta^*_{n\sigma^2}) < \infty$, *then* $\overline{u(\infty)}$ *is extended Bayes.*

Proof. Let $\bar{p} \in \Gamma$ be such that

$$\begin{aligned} \bar{p}_j &= 0, & j &\neq k, \\ &= \bar{p}_k \not\equiv 0, & j &= k. \end{aligned}$$

Then define $\bar{\omega} = \overline{u(n)} + \bar{p}$. From Eq. (E.9)

$$\int \rho_{k+1}\, d\Omega(x_{k+1}, \tilde{x}_{k+1}, \xi_k) + \alpha_k \Big|_{\bar{u}=\bar{\omega}}$$

$$= \rho_k + K_k \int M_k(\bar{p}_k)^2 \prod_{i=0}^{k} \delta_i \prod_{i=0}^{k-1} p(\eta_i) \prod_{i=0}^{k} p(\tilde{x}_i \mid \tilde{x}_{i-1})$$

$$\times \left[\left(\frac{1}{\sqrt{2\pi\sigma}}\right)^{k-1} \exp\{a_k\} + O\left(\frac{1}{\sqrt{n}}\right)\right] p(\xi_0)\, d\Omega(\eta^{k-1}).$$

By definition

$$\sum_{i=k}^{N} R_i(\bar{u}, \theta^*_{n\sigma^2}) = \sum_{i=k}^{N} \int \alpha_i \beta_i\, d\Omega(v^i, \tilde{x}^i, \xi^{i-1}, x^i).$$

For the Bayes policy this equation can be written in the form

$$\sum_{i=k}^{N} R_i(\overline{u(n)}, \theta^*_{n\sigma^2}) = \int \rho_k \beta_{k-1}\, d\Omega(v^{k-1}, \tilde{x}^k, \xi^{k-1}, x^k).$$

Consequently,

$$\sum_{i=k}^{N} R_i(\bar{\omega}, \theta^*_{n\sigma^2}) = \int \rho_k \beta_{k-1} \, d\Omega(v^{k-1}, \tilde{x}^k, \xi^{k-1}, x^k)$$

$$+ K_k \int M_k(\bar{p}_k)^2 \beta_{k-1} \prod_{i=0}^{k} \delta_i \prod_{i=0}^{k-1} p(\eta_i)$$

$$\times \prod_{i=0}^{k} p(\tilde{x}_i \mid \tilde{x}_{i-1}) \left[\left(\frac{1}{\sqrt{2\pi\sigma}} \right)^{k-1} \exp\{a_k\} + O\left(\frac{1}{\sqrt{n}} \right) \right]$$

$$\times p(\xi_0) \, d\Omega(\eta^{k-1}, v^{k-1}, \tilde{x}^k, \xi^{k-1}, x^k).$$

By hypothesis $\lim_{n\to\infty} H(\overline{u(n)}, \theta^*_{n\sigma^2}) < \infty$, and thus, K_k and M_k are bounded. We may write

$$K_k < K,$$

$$M_k < M.$$

Choose $\bar{p}_k$ such that

$$\| p_k \|^2 < \delta KM \int \prod_{i=0}^{k-1} \delta(v_i - \overline{u(\infty)}_i) \prod_{i=0}^{k} \delta_i \prod_{i=0}^{k-1} p(\eta_i)$$

$$\times \prod_{i=0}^{k} p(\tilde{x}_i \mid \tilde{x}_{i-1}) \left[\left(\frac{1}{\sqrt{2\pi\sigma}} \right)^{k-1} \exp\{a_k\} \right] p(\xi_0)$$

$$\times d\Omega(\eta^{k-1}, v^{k-1}, \tilde{x}^k, \xi^{k-1}).$$

Then there exists an n large enough to insure that

$$\left| \sum_{i=k}^{N} R_i(\bar{\omega}, \theta^*_{n\sigma^2}) - \sum_{i=k}^{N} R_i(\overline{u(n)}, \theta^*_{n\sigma^2}) \right| < \delta.$$

Therefore, by Theorem 5.1 $\overline{u(\infty)}$ is extended Bayes. ▼

We next wish to derive a sufficient condition under which $\overline{u(\infty)}$ is admissible. Before treating the admissibility, let us turn to the related problem of the continuity of the cost function.

Theorem 5.3. *Let the object to be controlled be described by the equation*

$$x_{j+1} = f_j(\xi^j, x^j), \qquad x_q = x(q). \tag{5.17}$$

Let $h(x, v)$ *be continuous in* x. *If*

$$\| E(x_j \mid \theta)\| < \infty, \qquad 0 \leqslant j \leqslant N,$$

and

$$\| E(\xi_i x_j \mid \theta)\| < \infty, \qquad 0 \leqslant i, \ \ j \leqslant N,$$

for all $\theta \in \Theta$, *then* $H(\bar{v}, \theta)$ *is continuous in* θ.

Proof. By hypothesis

$$x_{j+1} = f_j(\xi^j, x^j),$$
$$x_q = x(q).$$

The solution to this difference equation can be written in the form

$$x_k = F_k(\xi^{k-1}, x(q)).$$

Therefore,

$$E(x_k \mid \theta_1) - E(x_k \mid \theta_2) = \int F_k(\xi^{k-1}, x(q))[p(\xi^{k-1} \mid \theta_1) - p(\xi^{k-1} \mid \theta_2)] \, d\Omega(\xi^{k-1}).$$

The sequence ξ^j is a Wiener process with Gaussian increments and is described by Eq. (5.3). Therefore,

$$p(\xi^j \mid \theta) = \prod_{i=1}^{j} p(\xi_i \mid \xi_{i-j}, \theta) p(\xi_0)$$

$$= \left(\frac{1}{\sqrt{2\pi}\sigma}\right)^j \exp\left\{-\frac{1}{2\sigma^2} \sum_{i=1}^{j} (\xi_i - \xi_{i-1} - \theta)^2\right\} p(\xi_0).$$

We can write

$$p(\xi^j \mid \theta_1) - p(\xi^j \mid \theta_2) = \left(\frac{1}{\sqrt{2\pi}\sigma}\right)^j \left[\exp\left\{-\frac{1}{2\sigma^2} \sum_{i=1}^{j} (\xi_i - \xi_{i-1} - \theta_1)^2\right\}\right.$$

$$\left. - \exp\left\{-\frac{1}{2\sigma^2} \sum_{i=1}^{j} (\xi_i - \xi_{i-1} - \theta_2)^2\right\}\right] p(\xi_0).$$

The following identity can easily be verified:

$$\exp\left\{-\frac{1}{2\sigma^2}\sum_{i=1}^{j}(\xi_i-\xi_{i-1}-\theta_1)^2\right\}-\exp\left\{-\frac{1}{2\sigma^2}\sum_{i=1}^{j}(\xi_i-\xi_{i-1}-\theta_2)^2\right\}$$

$$=\exp\left\{-\frac{1}{2\sigma^2}\sum_{i=1}^{j}(\xi_i-\xi_{i-1}-\theta_2)^2\right\}$$

$$\times\left[\exp\left\{-\frac{1}{2\sigma^2}\left(2(\theta_2-\theta_1)\sum_{i=1}^{j}(\xi_i-\xi_{i-1})+j(\theta_1{}^2-\theta_2{}^2)\right)\right\}-1\right].$$

Thus,

$$\exp\left\{-\frac{1}{2\sigma^2}\sum_{i=1}^{j}(\xi_i-\xi_{i-1}-\theta_1)^2\right\}$$

$$=\exp\left\{-\frac{1}{2\sigma^2}\sum_{i=1}^{j}(\xi_i-\xi_{i-1}-\theta_2)^2\right\}$$

$$+\frac{\theta_2-\theta_1}{2\sigma^2}\left[2\sum_{i=1}^{j}(\xi_i-\xi_{i-1})-j\theta_1-j\theta_2\right]$$

$$\times\exp\left\{-\frac{1}{2\sigma^2}\sum_{i=1}^{j}(\xi_i-\xi_{i-1}-\theta_2)^2\right\}+o(\theta_2-\theta_1).$$

Therefore,

$$p(\xi^j\mid\theta_1)-p(\xi^j\mid\theta_2)=\left(\frac{1}{\sqrt{2\pi}\sigma}\right)^j\frac{(\theta_2-\theta_1)}{2\sigma^2}\left[-j(\theta_2+\theta_1)+2\sum_{i=1}^{j}(\xi_i-\xi_{i-1})\right]$$

$$\times\exp\left\{-\frac{1}{2\sigma^2}\sum_{i=1}^{j}(\xi_i-\xi_{i-1}-\theta_2)^2\right\}p(\xi_0)$$

$$+o(\theta_2-\theta_1).$$

Retaining only first-order terms, we have

$$E(x_k\mid\theta_1)-E(x_k\mid\theta_2)$$

$$\simeq\frac{\theta_2-\theta_1}{2\sigma^2}\left[\int(-k+1)(\theta_2+\theta_1)F_k(\xi^{k-1},x(q))p(\xi^{k-1}\mid\theta_2)\,d\Omega(\xi^{k-1}),\right.$$

$$\left.+2\int\sum_{i=1}^{k-1}(\xi_i-\xi_{i-1})F_k(\xi^{k-1},x(q))p(\xi^{k-1}\mid\theta_2)\,d\Omega(\xi^{k-1})\right]$$

$$\simeq\frac{\theta_2-\theta_1}{2\sigma^2}[(-k+1)(\theta_1+\theta_2)E\{x_k\mid\theta_2\}+2E\{\xi_{k-1}x_k\mid\theta_2\}-2E\{\xi_0x_k\mid\theta_2\}].$$

But each term in the above bracket is bounded, by hypothesis, and thus, for every $\epsilon > 0$, there exists a $\delta > 0$ such that if $| \theta_2 - \theta_1 | < \delta$,

$$\| E(x_k \mid \theta_1) - E(x_k \mid \theta_2) \| < \epsilon.$$

Since the performance functional is continuous in x_k, $H(\bar{v}, \theta)$ is continuous in θ. ▼

Before we go on it is important to relate the results of this theorem to the system described by Eqs. (5.1), (5.4), and (5.5). By augmenting the state vector with the command input, the system equations can be written in the form

$$\hat{x}_{j+1} = \hat{\phi}_j(\xi_j)x_j + \hat{\Delta}_j v_j + \hat{\Theta}_j \eta_j . \tag{5.18}$$

In the same manner a composite disturbance vector can be formed by defining

$$\hat{\xi}_j = \begin{bmatrix} \xi_j \\ \eta_j \end{bmatrix}. \tag{5.19}$$

To complete the identification of the systems described by Eqs. (5.17) and (5.18) consider the form of the pure control policies $\bar{u} \in \Gamma$.

$$v_j = \bar{u}_j(\hat{x}^j, \hat{\xi}^{j-1}, v^{j-1}).$$

The solution of this difference equation can be written in the form

$$v_j = U_j(\hat{x}^j, \xi^j). \tag{5.20}$$

Substituting Eqs. (5.19) and (5.20) into Eq. (5.18), we have the result

$$\hat{x}_{j+1} = F_j(\hat{x}^j, \hat{\xi}^j).$$

From Eq. (5.5) it is evident that $h(x, v, \tilde{x})$ is continuous in $\hat{x}$, and the assumption that $H(\bar{v}, \theta) < \infty$ implies that $E\{\xi_i x_j \mid \theta\} < \infty$ and $E\{x_j \mid \theta\} < \infty$ for all $\theta \in \Theta$. Thus, the system under analysis in this chapter is a member of the set for which $H(\bar{v}, \theta)$ is continuous in θ.

Since the support of $\theta^*_{n\sigma^2}$ is the real line for all $n > 0$, it is clear that all of $\overline{u(n)}$ are admissible. Because $\overline{u(\infty)}$ is the limit of a sequence of admissible rules, one might surmise that $\overline{u(\infty)}$ is, itself, admissible. Unfortunately, the same reasoning which was used in the proof of

Theorem 2.3 cannot be used to verify this result because the support of $\lim_{n\to\infty} \theta^*_{n\sigma^2}$ is empty. Because of this, simple convergence of $\overline{u(n)}$ is not, in general, sufficient to guarantee the admissibility of $\overline{u(\infty)}$. In a sense, we must prove that the Bayes costs converge faster to their limit than the *a priori* distributions approach zero.

Theorem 5.4. *Let $\overline{u(n)} \in \Gamma$ be a Bayes control policy with respect to $\theta^*_{n\sigma^2} =$ Nor$(0, n\sigma^2)$. Let $\overline{u(\infty)} \in \Gamma$ be such that*

$$\lim_{n\to\infty} \sqrt{n}\, | H(\overline{u(\infty)}, \theta^*_{n\sigma^2}) - H(\overline{u(n)}, \theta^*_{n\sigma^2})| = 0.$$

Then, if $H(\bar{v}, \theta)$ is continuous in θ, $\overline{u(\infty)}$ is admissible.

Proof. Assume $\overline{u(\infty)}$ is not admissible. Then there exists an $\bar{S}_0 \in \Gamma$ such that $H(\overline{u(\infty)}, \theta) - H(\bar{S}_0, \theta) \geqslant 0$ for all $\theta \in \Theta$, and there exists $\theta_0 \in \Theta$ such that $H(\overline{u(\infty)}, \theta_0) > H(\bar{S}_0, \theta_0)$. Since $H(\bar{v}, \theta)$ is continuous in θ, there exists a $\delta > 0$ such that if

$$\eta = H(\overline{u(\infty)}, \theta_0) - H(\bar{S}_0, \theta_0),$$

then

$$H(\overline{u(\infty)}, \theta) - H(\bar{S}_0, \theta) > \frac{\eta}{2}$$

for all $\theta \in (\theta_0 - \delta, \theta_0 + \delta)$. Hence,

$$\int_{-\infty}^{\infty} [H(\overline{u(\infty)}, \theta) - H(\bar{S}_0, \theta)]\, d\theta^*_{n\sigma^2} > \frac{\eta}{2} \frac{1}{\sqrt{2\pi n}\sigma} \int_{\theta_0-\delta}^{\theta_0+\delta} \exp\left\{-\frac{\theta^2}{2n\sigma^2}\right\} d\theta.$$

Choose a real number M such that if $n > M$

$$\int_{\theta_0-\delta}^{\theta_0+\delta} \exp\left\{-\frac{\theta^2}{2n\sigma^2}\right\} d\theta^*_{n\sigma} > \delta.$$

Then, if $n > M$,

$$\int [H(\overline{u(\infty)}, \theta) - H(\bar{S}_0, \theta)]\, d\theta^*_{n\sigma^2} > \frac{\eta\delta}{2\sigma\sqrt{2\pi n}}.$$

Or equivalently,

$$H(\bar{S}_0, \theta^*_{n\sigma^2}) \leqslant H(\overline{u(\infty)}, \theta^*_{n\sigma^2}) - \frac{\eta\delta}{2\sigma\sqrt{2\pi n}}.$$

We can now write

$$H(\bar{S}_0, \theta^*_{n\sigma^2}) - H(\overline{u(n)}, \theta^*_{n\sigma^2}) \leqslant H(\overline{u(\infty)}, \theta^*_{n\sigma^2}) - H(\overline{u(n)}, \theta^*_{n\sigma^2}) - \frac{\eta\delta}{2\sigma\sqrt{2\pi n}}.$$

But this implies that given any $\epsilon > 0$ there exists M_1 such that if $n > M_1$,

$$H(\bar{S}_0, \theta^*_{n\sigma^2}) - H(\overline{u(n)}, \theta^*_{n\sigma^2}) \leqslant \left(\epsilon - \frac{\eta\delta}{2\sigma\sqrt{2\pi}}\right)\frac{1}{\sqrt{n}}.$$

If we choose $\epsilon < \dfrac{\eta\delta}{2\sigma\sqrt{2\pi}}$,

$$H(\bar{S}_0, \theta^*_{n\sigma^2}) - H(\overline{u(n)}, \theta^*_{n\sigma^2}) < 0.$$

This contradicts the assertion that $\overline{u(n)}$ is Bayes with respect to $\theta^*_{n\sigma^2}$, and therefore $\overline{u(\infty)}$ is admissible. ▼

Theorem 5.4 provides a sufficient condition for the admissibility of $\overline{u(\infty)}$ for a rather arbitrary plant and performance measure. Unfortunately, we see in Eq. (5.13) that the system under investigation in this chapter satisfies the weaker condition:

$$\lim_{n\to\infty} \sqrt{n}\,[H(\overline{u(\infty)}, \theta^*_{n\sigma^2}) - H(\overline{u(n)}, \theta^*_{n\sigma^2})] = C < \infty.$$

For this reason the system linearity and the quadratic nature of the performance criterion must be employed to prove that $\overline{u(\infty)}$ is admissible

Theorem 5.5 *$\overline{u(\infty)}$ is admissible.*

Proof. The proof that $\overline{u(\infty)}$ is admissible will proceed by contradiction. Assume that $\overline{u(\infty)}$ is not admissible. Then there exists an $s^* \in \Gamma^*$ such that

$$H(s^*, \theta) \leqslant H(\overline{u(\infty)}, \theta)$$

for all $\theta \in \Theta$, and there exists a $\theta_0 \in \Theta$ such that

$$H(s^*, \theta_0) < H(\overline{u(\infty)}, \theta_0).$$

Let us first prove that if such an $s^* \in \Gamma^*$ exists, then there exists an $\bar{s} \in \Gamma$ which also is better than $\overline{u(\infty)}$. From Eq. (5.1) it is evident that the state vector at any time $t = j\Delta$ can be written in the form

$$x_k = \prod_{i=0}^{k-1} \phi_i x_0 + \sum_{i=1}^{k} \left(\prod_{j=0}^{k-i-1} \phi_j \right) (\Delta_{i-1} v_{i-1} + \Theta_{i-1} \eta_{i-1})$$

where $\prod_{i=0}^{-1} \phi_i = 1$. Therefore,

$$(\tilde{x}_k - Hx_k)^2 = \tilde{x}_k^2 - 2\tilde{x}_k H \left[\prod_{i=0}^{k-1} \phi_i x_0 + \sum_{i=1}^{k} \left(\prod_{j=0}^{k-i-1} \phi_j \right) (\Delta_{i-1} v_{i-1} + \Theta_{i-1} \eta_{i-1}) \right]$$

$$+ \left[H \prod_{i=0}^{k-1} \phi_i x_0 + H \sum_{i=0}^{k} \left(\prod_{j=0}^{k-i-1} \phi_j \right) (\Delta_{i-1} v_{i-1} + \Theta_{i-1} \eta_{i-1}) \right]^2 .$$

The explicit expression for the criterion functional becomes

$$\sum_{k=0}^{N} (x_k - Hx_k)^2 + \beta_k v_k^2 = \sum_{k=0}^{N} \left\{ \tilde{x}_k^2 - 2\tilde{x}_k H \left[\prod_{i=0}^{k-1} \phi_i x_0 + \sum_{i=1}^{k} \prod_{j=0}^{k-i-1} \phi_j \Theta_{i-1} \eta_{i-1} \right] \right.$$

$$\left. + \left(H \prod_{i=0}^{k-1} \phi_i x_0 + H \sum_{i=1}^{k} \left(\prod_{j=0}^{k-i-1} \phi_j \right) \Theta_{i-1} \eta_{i-1} \right)^2 \right\}$$

$$-2 \sum_{k=0}^{N} \left\{ \tilde{x}_k H \sum_{i=1}^{k} \left(\prod_{j=0}^{k-i-1} \phi_j \right) \Delta_{i-1} v_{i-1} \right.$$

$$- \left(H \prod_{k=i=0}^{k-1} \phi_i x_0 + H \sum_{i=1}^{k} \left(\prod_{j=0}^{k-i-1} \phi_i \right) \Theta_{i-1} \eta_{i-1} \right)$$

$$\left. \times \left(H \sum_{i=1}^{k} \left(\prod_{i=0}^{k-i-1} \phi_j \right) \Delta_{i-1} v_{i-1} \right) \right\}$$

$$+ \sum_{k=0}^{N} \left\{ \beta_k v_k^2 + \left(H \sum_{i=1}^{K} \left(\prod_{j=0}^{k-i-1} \phi_j \right) \Delta_{i-1} v_{i-1} \right)^2 \right\} .$$

The criterion functional, $h(x, \bar{v}, \tilde{x})$, is obviously convex in v^N, and consequently, Lemma 2.2 can be employed to deduce that $H(\bar{u}, \theta)$ is convex in $\bar{u}$. By Theorem 2.2 there exists an $\bar{s} \in \Gamma$ which is as good as s^*, and thus, better than $\overline{u(\infty)}$.

Since $\bar{s}$ is better than $\overline{u(\infty)}$, it must be true that

$$H(\bar{s}, \theta^*_{n\sigma^2}) \leqslant H(\overline{u(\infty)}, \theta_{n\sigma^2})$$

for all $n \geqslant 0$. Define $\overline{u(\infty)} - \bar{s} = \bar{t}$. Let us now evaluate the Bayes cost of $\bar{s}$ with respect to $\theta^*_{n\sigma^2}$. By analogy with Eqs. (4.16) and (4.17) it is clear that $H(\bar{s}, \theta^*_{n\sigma^2})$ is generated by a recurrence formula of the form

$$\lambda_{N+1} = 0$$

$$\lambda_{N-j} = \alpha_{N-j} + \int \lambda_{N-j+1}\, d\Omega(x_{N-j+1}, \tilde{x}_{N-j+1}, \xi_{N-j}) \Big|_{\bar{u}_{N-j}=\bar{s}_{N-j}}.$$

and

$$H(\bar{s}, \theta^*_{n\sigma^2}) = \int \lambda_q p(\tilde{x}^q, \xi^{q-1})\, d\Omega(\tilde{x}^q, \xi^{q-1}).$$

If $\bar{s}$ is better than $\overline{u(\infty)}$, then must be true that $\lim_{n\to\infty} E\{\lambda_q\} \leqslant \lim_{n\to\infty} E\{\rho_q(n)\}$ since the latter quantity is the "Bayes" cost of $\overline{u(\infty)}$. From Eq. (5.1) it is evident that the state of the system is independent of $\bar{t}_N$. Since $\overline{u(\infty)} \not\equiv \bar{s}$, there must exist a $j \in [q, N-1]$ such that $\bar{t}_j \not\equiv 0$ and $\bar{t}_i \equiv 0$ for all $i > j$. From Eq. (E.9) we see that

$$\lim_{n\to\infty} \lambda_j = \lim_{n\to\infty} \rho_j + K_j \int M_j(\bar{t}_j)^2 \prod_{i=0}^{j} \delta_i \prod_{i=0}^{j-1} p(\eta_i)$$

$$\times \prod_{i=0}^{j} p(\tilde{x}_i \mid \tilde{x}_{i-1}) \left[\left(\frac{1}{\sqrt{2\pi}\sigma} \right)^{j-1} \exp\{a_j\} \right] d\Omega(\eta^{j-1}).$$

Since all of the factors in the second term are positive it must be true that

$$\lim_{n\to\infty} \lambda_j > \lim_{n\to\infty} \rho_j$$

for all values of its argument unless $\bar{t}_j = 0$ almost surely in Z_j. Let us assume $\lim_{n\to\infty} \lambda_k > \lim_{n\to\infty} \rho_k$. Then

$$\lambda_{k-1} = \alpha_{k-1} + \int \lambda_k\, d\Omega(x_k, \tilde{x}_k, \xi_{k-1}) \Big|_{\bar{u}_k=\bar{s}_k}$$

$$\lim_{n\to\infty} \lambda_{k-1} > \lim_{n\to\infty} \alpha_j + \int \lim_{n\to\infty} \rho_k\, d\Omega(x_k, \tilde{x}_k, \xi_{k-1}) \Big|_{\bar{u}_k=\bar{s}_k}$$

$$> \inf_{\bar{u}_k} \left[\lim_{n\to\infty} \alpha_{k-1} + \int \lim_{n\to\infty} \rho_k\, d\Omega(x_k, \tilde{x}_k, \xi_{k-1}) \right].$$

Thus there exists an n such that $\lambda_{k-1} > \rho_{k-1}$.

By induction there exists an n such that $\lambda_q(n) > \rho_q(n)$, unless $\bar{t}_j = 0$ almost surely for all $j \in [q, N-1]$. This cannot be true, because by hypothesis there exists a $\theta \in \Theta$ for which $\bar{s}$ is better than $\overline{u(\infty)}$. Thus we have a contradiction to the hypothesis that $\bar{s}$ is better than $\overline{u(\infty)}$. ▼

In this section we have shown that $\overline{u(\infty)}$ has several strong optimality properties. It is admissible and "Bayes" with respect to the *a priori* "distribution" for θ. In problems for which the *a priori* information is meager a minimax control policy has much intuitive appeal. For the general system described by Eq. (5.1) such a control rule is quite difficult to evaluate directly since the form of $H(\bar{u}, \theta^*)$ does not permit one to apply the $\sup_{\theta^* \in \Theta^*}$ operator in any convenient way. For some systems, however, it can be shown indirectly that $\overline{u(\infty)}$ is a minimax policy. Since $\overline{u(\infty)}$ is an extended Bayes control rule, we need only show that $\overline{u(\infty)}$ is an equalizer policy to prove the desired result, and in the next section a process will examined for which $\overline{u(\infty)}$ is an equalizer.

5. A Certain Class of Markov Systems

In the previous sections of this chapter we have considered the general linear system characterized by the linear difference relation given by Eq. (5.1). In this section a system will be analyzed which is described by a particular form of this equation:

$$\begin{aligned} z_{j+1} + a_{j,1} z_j + \cdots + a_{j,n} z_{j-n+1} &= v_j + \eta_j\,, \qquad j = 0, \ldots, N, \\ z_i = z(i), &\qquad -n \leqslant i \leqslant 2. \end{aligned} \tag{5.21}$$

The $a_{i,j}$, $0 \leqslant i \leqslant N$, $1 \leqslant j \leqslant n$, will be assumed to have a specific structure.

$$\begin{aligned} a_{j,i} &= \lambda_{j,i}\,, \quad \text{independent of } \xi_j\,, \qquad 0 \leqslant j \leqslant N, \quad i \neq m, \\ &= \alpha_j \xi_j + \beta_j\,, \qquad\qquad\qquad\qquad 0 \leqslant j \leqslant N, \quad i = m. \end{aligned}$$

We are, thus, concerned with a plant which is described by a time-variable linear difference equation in which all of the parameters of the incremental transition matrix are deterministic with the exception of one. This one is linear in ξ_j. The index of performance will be

$$h(\tilde{x}^N, z^N, v^N) = \sum_{i=2}^{N} (\tilde{x}_i - z_i)^2 + v_N{}^2,$$

where $\tilde{x}$ is a Wiener process described by Eq. (5.4).

Equation (5.21) can be rewritten in a form which conforms to the earlier notation.

$$x_{j+1} = \phi_j x_j + \Delta_j v_j + \Theta_j \eta_j, \qquad 0 \leqslant j \leqslant N,$$
$$x_2 = x(2),$$

where

$$x_j = \begin{bmatrix} z_{j-n+1} \\ \vdots \\ z_{j-1} \\ z_j \end{bmatrix}, \qquad \Delta_j = \begin{bmatrix} 0 \\ \vdots \\ 0 \\ 1 \end{bmatrix}, \qquad \Theta_j = \begin{bmatrix} 0 \\ \vdots \\ 0 \\ 1 \end{bmatrix}. \tag{5.22}$$

$$\phi_j = \begin{bmatrix} 0 & 1 & \cdots & 0 \\ 0 & 0 & \cdots & 0 \\ 0 & 0 & 1 & \\ \vdots & & & \\ 0 & & & 1 \\ -a_{j,n} & -a_{j,n-1} & \cdots & -a_{j,1} \end{bmatrix}.$$

Then, if we choose

$$H = [0, \ldots, 0, 1], \tag{5.23}$$

we place the criterion of performance in the form

$$h(x^N, v, \tilde{x}^N) = \sum_{i=2}^{N} (\tilde{x}_i - Hx_i)^2 + v_N{}^2.$$

The control policy $\overline{u(\infty)}$ can be taken directly from Eq. (5.13). Note that Δ_j is independent of ξ^j and that $\beta_j = 0$ for all $j \in [0, N-1]$. Consequently

$$M_j = \Delta^T(\overline{P_{j+1}} + \sqrt{\frac{j}{N}}\, H^T H)\Delta,$$

and therefore,

$$\overline{u(\infty)_j} = -\left(\overline{x_j{}^T\phi_j{}^T P_{j+1}}\,\Delta - \sqrt{\frac{j}{N}}\,\tilde{x}_j + \sqrt{\frac{j}{N}}\,\bar{\phi}_j x_j + \frac{1}{2}\overline{Q_{j+1}}\,\Delta\tilde{x}_j\right)\left(\Delta\overline{P_{j+1}}\,\Delta + \sqrt{\frac{j}{N}}\right)^{-1}, \qquad 2 \leqslant j \leqslant N-1,$$

$$= 0, \qquad j = N.$$

We will now establish that for the class of systems described by Eq. (5.21), the control policy $\overline{u(\infty)}$ is minimax. It has already been demonstrated that $\overline{u(\infty)}$ is an extended Bayes policy so we need only show that it is an equalizer.

First an induction argument will be used to prove that L_j, P_j, R_j, and Q_j are independent of ξ^j for $2 \leqslant j \leqslant N$. From Eq. (E.8) it is apparent that L_j is independent of ξ^j if R_{j+1} and P_{j+1} are, so the problem is reduced to analyzing R_j, P_j, and Q_j.

From Eqs. (5.22) and (5.23) we see that

$$H\Delta = 1.$$

Consequently, Eq. (5.11) can be simplified for this special case:

$$M_{N-1} = 1,$$

$$Q_{N-1} = -2H\overline{\phi_{N-1}} - 2H\overline{\phi_{N-1}} = 0,$$

$$R_{N-1} = 2,$$

and

$$P_{N-1} = \overline{\phi_{N-1}^T H^T H \phi_{N-1}} - \overline{\phi_{N-1}^T}\, H^T H\, \overline{\phi_{N-1}}\,.$$

From Eq. (5.22) it is evident that

$$\phi_{N-1}^T H^T H \phi_{N-1} = [a_{N-1,n}\,, \ldots, a_{N-1,1}]^T [a_{N-1\,n}\,, \ldots, a_{N-1,1}].$$

Nonzero terms in P_{N-1} occur only for the difference

$$\overline{(a_{N-1,m})^2} - (\overline{a_{N-1,m}})^2.$$

Using Eq. (F.4), P_{N-1} can be written as

$$(P_{N-1})_{ij} = \frac{N-1}{N-2}\,\sigma^2\alpha_{N-1}^2\,, \qquad i = j = m,$$

$$= 0 \qquad \text{otherwise.}$$

Clearly, P_{N-1} is diagonal and independent of ξ^{N-1}. Appendix F proves that if R_{N-1} is independent of $\xi^N, Q_{N-1} = 0$, and P_{N-1} is diagonal and independent of ξ^N, then:

$$\begin{aligned} &(1)\quad Q_j = 0, \\ &(2)\quad R_j \text{ is independent of } \xi^N, \text{ and} \\ &(3)\quad P_j \text{ is independent of } \xi^N \text{ and is diagonal,} \end{aligned} \tag{5.24}$$

for all integers j in the interval $[2, N-1]$.

This result certainly indicates that $\overline{u(\infty)}$ is an equalizer policy because the expected value of $\sum_{i=k}^{N} (\tilde{x}_i - Hx_i)^2$ is independent of ξ^k. One might suppose that the expected value of the cost of the process in the time interval $[k, N]$ when conditioned on z_k should be functionally dependent on the *a posteriori* distribution function for θ at time k. Since this distribution function is a function of ξ^{k-1}, it might therefore be inferred that $E\{\sum_{i=k}^{N} (\tilde{x}_i - Hx_i)^2 \mid \xi^{k-1}\}$ should be a function of ξ^{k-1}. But, in fact, for the system under analysis this conditional expectation does not depend on ξ^{k-1}, and therefore does not depend on the *a posteriori* distribution for θ.

To make the reasoning in the previous paragraph more precise we proceed as follows.

Theorem 5.6. *$\overline{u(\infty)}$ is an equalizer policy.*

Proof. If $\overline{u(\infty)}$ is an equalizer, then it must satisfy the relation (see Definition 3.4)

$$H(\overline{u(\infty)}, \theta) = C$$

for all $\theta \in \Theta$. The performance index $H(\overline{u(\infty)}, \theta)$ is defined by the equation

$$H(\overline{u(\infty)}, \theta) = E\{h(x, \overline{u(\infty)}(z), \tilde{x})\}.$$

The functional $h(x, \overline{u(\infty)}(z), \tilde{x})$ is a random number with probability distribution function which may depend on θ. If, however, the probability distribution of $h(x, \overline{u(\infty)}(z), x)$ is independent of θ, the expected value of h must also be independent of θ. Consider the arguments of $h(x, \overline{u(\infty)}(z), \tilde{x})$. From Eq. (5.5) we see that

$$h(x, \overline{u(\infty)}(z), \tilde{x}) = \sum_{i=q}^{N} (\tilde{x}_i - Hx_i)^2.$$

The command input, $\tilde{x}$, is a scalar Wiener process which is completely described statistically by Eq. (5.4). Thus, the probability distribution of $\tilde{x}_i$ is certainly independent of θ.

Consequently, if h is to be dependent on θ, then it must be the case that the distribution function for x_i depends upon θ for some $i \in [q, N]$. Since it is the initial condition vector, x_q is independent of θ. Assume, therefore, that x_j is independent of θ for some $j \in [q, N]$. We will now prove that x_{j+1} must also be independent.

It is always true that

$$p(x_{j+1}) = \int p(x_{j+1} \mid x_j)p(x_j)\, d\Omega(x_j).$$

The induction hypothesis specifies that $p(x_j)$ is independent of θ, and consequently, $p(x_{j+1})$ will also be independent if $p(x_{j+1} \mid x_j)$ is independent of θ.

From Eqs. (5.17) and (5.24), we have the result

$$\begin{aligned}\overline{u(\infty)_j} &= -\frac{(\Delta^T P_{j+1}\bar{\phi}_j x_j - \sqrt{j/N}\,(\tilde{x}_j - H\bar{\phi}_j x_j)}{\Delta^T P_{j+1}\Delta + \sqrt{j/N}}, \qquad q \leqslant j \leqslant N-1,\\ &= 0, \qquad j = N.\end{aligned}$$

Substituting this equation into Eq. (5.1), we have

$$\begin{aligned}x_{j+1} = \phi_j x_j &- \frac{\Delta(\Delta^T P_{j+1}\bar{\phi}_j x_j + \sqrt{j/N}\,H\bar{\phi}_j x_j)}{\Delta^T P_{j+1}\Delta + \sqrt{j/N}} + \Theta_j\eta_j\\ &+ \frac{\Delta\sqrt{j/N}\,\tilde{x}_j}{\Delta P_{j+1}\Delta + \sqrt{j/N}}.\end{aligned} \tag{5.25}$$

The last two terms in the above expression are assuredly independent of θ. Therefore, if the conditional probability distribution of x_{j+1} depends on θ, this dependence must enter through the first two terms.

Rewriting these terms, we have

$$\begin{aligned}\phi_j x_j &- \frac{\Delta(\Delta^T P_{j+1}\bar{\phi}_j x_j + \sqrt{j/N}\,H\bar{\phi}_j x_j)}{\Delta^T P_{j+1}\Delta + \sqrt{j/N}}\\ &= \frac{[\Delta^T P_{j+1}\Delta\phi_j - \Delta\,\Delta^T P_{j+1}\phi_j + \sqrt{j/N}\,(\phi_j - \Delta H\bar{\phi}_j)]x_j}{\Delta^T P_{j+1}\Delta + \sqrt{j/N}}.\end{aligned}$$

Denote the element of the matrix M in row i and column j by $(M)_{ij}$. In Appendix F it is shown that P_{j+1} is a diagonal matrix independent of ξ^N. Therefore,

$$\Delta^T P_{j+1} \Delta = (P_{j+1})_{nn},$$

$$\begin{aligned}(\Delta\Delta^T P_{j+1})_{ij} &= (P_{j+1})_{nn}, \qquad & i = j = n,\\ &= 0 & \text{otherwise,}\end{aligned}$$

and

$$\begin{aligned}(\Delta\Delta^T P_{j+1}\bar{\phi})_{ij} &= 0, \qquad & i \neq n,\\ &= (P_{j+1})_{nn}(\bar{\phi}_j)_{ij}, & i = n,\end{aligned}$$

hence

$$\begin{aligned}(\Delta^T P_{j+1}\Delta\phi_j - \Delta\Delta^T P_{j+1}\bar{\phi}_j)_{ij} &= (P_{j+1})_{nn}(\bar{\phi}_j)_{ij}, \qquad & i \neq n,\\ &= 0, & i = n, \quad j \neq m,\\ &= (P_{j+1})_{nn}\alpha_j(\xi_j - \bar{\xi}_j), & i = n, \quad j = m.\end{aligned}$$

In an analogous manner one can show that

$$\begin{aligned}(\phi_j - \Delta H\bar{\phi}_j)_{ij} &= (\phi_j)_{ij}, \qquad & i \neq n,\\ &= 0. & i = n, \quad j \neq m,\\ &= \alpha_j(\xi_j - \bar{\xi}_j), & i = n, \quad j = m.\end{aligned}$$

From Eq. (5.16) is apparent that $(\phi)_{ij}$ is independent of θ if $i \neq n$ since the only nonzero elements of this part of the matrix are constants. Therefore, if $p(x_{j+1} \mid x_j)$ depends on θ, the probability distribution function for $\xi_j - \bar{\xi}_j$ must depend on θ.

By definition

$$\bar{\xi}_j = \sqrt{\frac{j-1}{2\pi\sigma^2 j}} \int_{-\infty}^{\infty} \xi_j \exp\left\{-\frac{j-1}{2\sigma^2 j}\left(\xi_j - \xi_{j-1} - \frac{1}{j-1}\sum_{i=1}^{j-1}(\xi_i - \xi_{i-1})\right)^2\right\} d\xi_j$$

$$= \xi_{j-1} + \frac{1}{j-1}\sum_{i=1}^{j-1}(\xi_i - \xi_{i-1}).$$

Consequently,

$$\xi_j - \bar{\xi}_j = \xi_j - \xi_{j-1} - \frac{1}{j-1}\sum_{i=1}^{j-1}(\xi_i - \xi_{i-1}).$$

The random number represented by $\xi_j - \bar{\xi}_j$ is a Gaussian random variable since it is a linear combination of Gaussian random variables. To prove that $\xi_j - \bar{\xi}_j$ is independent of θ, we need only show that the mean and variance are independent of θ. From Eq. (5.3) it follows that

$$E\{\xi_i - \xi_{i-1}\} = \theta, \qquad i \in [1, N],$$

$$E\{(\xi_i - \xi_{i-1})(\xi_j - \xi_{j-1})\} = \theta^2, \qquad i \neq j,$$
$$= \sigma^2 + \theta^2, \qquad i = j \in [1, N].$$

Therefore,

$$E\{\xi_j - \bar{\xi}_j\} = 0$$

and

$$E\{(\xi_j - \bar{\xi}_j)^2\} = E\left\{(\xi_j - \xi_{j-1})^2 + \sum_{i=1}^{j-1}\left\{\frac{\xi_i - \xi_{i-1}}{j-1}\right\}^2\right\}$$
$$= \sigma^2\left(1 + \frac{1}{j-1}\right).$$

Therefore, $\xi_j - \bar{\xi}_j$ is independent of θ and $p(x_{j+1} \mid x_j)$ is independent of θ. By induction $p(x_j)$ is independent of θ for all integers $j \in [2, N]$, and $\overline{u(\infty)}$ is an equalizer policy. ▼

Since $\overline{u(\infty)}$ is both extended Bayes and an equalizer, we can use Theorem 3.9 to state that $\overline{u(\infty)}$ is minimax for this control problem. Equation (5.24) can be used to simplify the expression of $\overline{u(\infty)}$:

$$\overline{u(\infty)}_j = -\frac{(\Delta^T P_{j+1} + \sqrt{j/N}\, H)\bar{\phi}_j x_j - \sqrt{j/N}\, \tilde{x}_j}{\Delta^T P_{j+1}\Delta + \sqrt{j/N}}, \qquad 2 \leqslant j \leqslant N-1,$$
$$= 0, \qquad = N. \tag{5.26}$$

6. An Example

As an example of the theory of this chapter let us consider in some detail the system described by the equation

$$z_{j+1} + \xi_j z_j + \alpha z_{j-1} = v_j + \eta_j, \qquad j = 0, \ldots, N, \tag{5.27}$$
$$z_i = z(i), \qquad i = 0, 1, 2.$$

The state transition equation for the plant can be written as

$$\begin{bmatrix} z_j \\ z_{j+1} \end{bmatrix} = \begin{bmatrix} 0 & 1 \\ -\alpha & -\xi_j \end{bmatrix} \begin{bmatrix} z_{j-1} \\ z_j \end{bmatrix} + \begin{bmatrix} 0 \\ 1 \end{bmatrix} v_j + \begin{bmatrix} 0 \\ 1 \end{bmatrix} \eta_j .$$

From Eq. (5.26) it is clear that we need only evaluate $\overline{P_j}$ since this is the only unknown factor in the equation for $u(\infty)$. From Eqs. (5.11) and (D.4)

$$P_{N-1} = \left\{ \begin{bmatrix} \alpha^2 & \alpha\bar{\xi}_{N-1} \\ \alpha\bar{\xi}_{N-1} & \overline{\xi^2_{N-1}} \end{bmatrix} - \begin{bmatrix} \alpha^2 & \alpha\bar{\xi}_{N-1} \\ \alpha\bar{\xi}_{N-1} & \overline{(\xi_{N-1})}^2 \end{bmatrix} \right\}$$

$$= \begin{bmatrix} 0 & 0 \\ 0 & \dfrac{N-1}{N-2}\,\sigma^2 \end{bmatrix}$$

and

$$\overline{u(\infty)}_{N-1} = \tilde{x}_{N-1} + \alpha z_{N-2} + \bar{\xi}_{N-1} z_{N-1} .$$

It has already been proved in Appendix F that P_{N-j} is diagonal and independent of ξ^N. Consequently,

$$P_j = \begin{bmatrix} P_{j,11} & 0 \\ 0 & P_{j,22} \end{bmatrix}.$$

Substituting this equation into Eq. (E.7), one finds that

$$P_{N-j-1} = \begin{bmatrix} 0 & 0 \\ 0 & \left[P_{N-j,22} + \sqrt{\dfrac{N-j-1}{N}}\right]\left(\dfrac{N-j-1}{N-j-2}\right)\sigma^2 \end{bmatrix}.$$

Therefore, in order to specify P_{N-j} we need only solve the scalar difference equation:

$$P_{N-j-1,22} = \left[P_{N-j,22} + \sqrt{\frac{N-j-1}{N}}\right]\left(\frac{N-j-1}{N-j-2}\right)\sigma^2,$$

$$P_{N-1,22} = \left(\frac{N-1}{N-2}\right)\sigma^2.$$

This difference equation has for a solution

$$P_{N-j,22} = \left(\frac{N-1}{N-j-1}\right)(\sigma^2)^j + \sum_{i=2}^{j} \frac{N-i}{N-j-1}\sqrt{\frac{N-i}{N}}\,(\sigma^2)^{j-i+1}, \quad j \geqslant 1.$$

Placing this result in the equation for P_{N-j} gives

$$P_{N-j} = \begin{bmatrix} 0 & 0 \\ 0 & \dfrac{N-1}{N-j-1}(\sigma^2)^j + \sum_{i=2}^{j} \dfrac{N-i}{N-j-1}\sqrt{\dfrac{N-i}{N}}\,(\sigma^2)^{j-i+1} \end{bmatrix}. \tag{5.28}$$

Substituting Eq. (5.28) into Eq. (5.26), we obtain the minimax control policy for the system described by Eq. (5.27):

$$\begin{aligned} \overline{u(\infty)_j} &= \frac{\tilde{x}_j + (1 + K_j)(\alpha z_{j-1} + \xi_j z_j)}{1 + K_j}, \qquad 2 \leqslant j \leqslant N-1, \\ &= 0, \qquad\qquad j = N, \end{aligned} \tag{5.29}$$

where

$$K_j = \sqrt{\frac{N}{j}}\left[\frac{N-1}{j-1}(\sigma^2)^{N-j} + \sum_{i=2}^{N-j} \frac{N-i}{j-1}\sqrt{\frac{N-i}{N}}\,(\sigma^2)^{N-j-i+1}\right].$$

Let us now investigate two special cases of the system described by Eq. (5.27) in order to gain an intuitive feeling for the effect of the "learning" requirement implicit in this adaptive system. First consider the situation in which $\sigma^2 \ll 1/N$. In this case the *a posteriori* distribution for θ will give most of its measure to a small interval around the true value of θ before the control process begins. In this case

$$K_j = \frac{j}{j-1}\sigma^2 + O(\sigma^4).$$

Consequently,

$$\overline{u(\infty)_j} = \tilde{x}_j + \alpha z_{j-1} + \xi_j z_j - \frac{j}{j-1}\sigma^2 \tilde{x}_j + O(\sigma^4), \qquad 2 \leqslant j \leqslant N-1.$$

The only first-order effect of the unknown value of θ is a slight conservativeness with regard to reaching $\tilde{x}_j$. Instead of using the command input as a target, the control system uses $(1 - (j/j-1)\sigma^2)\tilde{x}_j$. Note that K_j is a differentiable function of j for all $j \geqslant 2$. Indeed,

$$\frac{dK_j}{dj} = -\frac{1}{(j-1)^2}\sigma^2 + O(\sigma^4)$$
$$< 0; \qquad j \geqslant 2.$$

Consequently, as time increases the controller's confidence in its estimate of θ increases and the controller becomes less conservative.

If $\sigma^2 = 0$, the problem becomes one of adapting to an unknown parameter. In this formulation of the problem there is sufficient information to solve for θ directly before the control process begins, and the only error in following the command input will occur because of randomness in $\tilde{x}^N$. On intuitive grounds alone, one would expect that

$$\bar{u}_j = \tilde{x}_j + \alpha z_{j-1} + \bar{\xi}_j z_j$$

is the optimal control for this system.

In the previous paragraph a system was analyzed in which sufficient information existed at the time control was initiated to make the effect of "learning" small. Now let us turn to the situation in which learning is difficult. That is, $\sigma^2 \gg 1$. Retaining only first-order terms, we have

$$K_j = \sqrt{\frac{N}{j}\frac{N-1}{j-1}}(\sigma^2)^{N-j}.$$

The equation for $\overline{u(\infty)}$ now becomes

$$\begin{aligned}\overline{u(\infty)}_j &= \frac{j-1}{N-1}\sqrt{\frac{j}{N}}\frac{\tilde{x}_j}{(\sigma^2)^{N-j}} + \alpha z_{j-1} + \bar{\xi}_j z_j, \qquad && 2 \leqslant j \leqslant N-1,\\ &= 0, && j = N.\end{aligned}$$

Under these circumstances more of the expected cost of the process will be due to the uncertainty about the plant transition properties than is due to the randomness of $\tilde{x}^N$. For this reason $\tilde{x}^N$ has only small influence in determining the control action. This influence increases as j increases indicating that more importance should be given to the actual value of $\tilde{x}_j$ as the estimate of θ improves.

7. Conclusion

In this chapter the theory of games has been applied to the synthesis of an optimal control policy for a process in which there exist unknown plant parameters. It is interesting that these parameters not only make the analytic problems associated with the design more complex, but they also introduce conceptual difficulties related to determining a rational set of design goals for control systems of this type. The basic impediment to a direct formulation of the criteria for an optimal control was the fact that the *a priori* information on θ could not be expressed as an element of Θ^*. For this reason we were led to attempt to approximate our prior knowledge with a sequence of elements of Θ^* which seemed to approach a suitable limit.

The main restriction which must be placed on the problem as posed is that the fixed element of the loop must be sufficiently well behaved to insure that the Bayes cost of $\overline{u(n)}$ is uniformly bounded. If this condition is satisfied, $\overline{u(\infty)}$ is an extended Bayes control policy and it is admissible. Under a more stringent restriction which relates to a linearity property of the system, $\overline{u(\infty)}$ can be shown to be minimax.

The work of his chapter has been restricted to the case of a scalar input and scalar control policy. This was done for clarity of presentation, and does not indicate an essential limitation of the method of approach. One basic restriction on the technique is the assumption that the past portion of ξ^N is available to the designer for use in determining the optimal control. This will always be the case if the system equation can be solved explicitly for ξ_j. If, however, only a function of ξ_j can be determined from the input-output records, then the problem becomes somewhat more complex. The conditions for a function of a Markov process to be a Markov process are rather strict, and for this reason the essential simplification which was obtained because of the Markov property of our system would, in general, be lost if ξ_j cannot be measured directly.

Discussion

The problem posed in this chapter is a discrete time, adaptive version of the class of systems studied in the following series of papers: Krasovskii [1], Katz and Krasovskii [2], Krasovskii and

Lidskii [3, 4], and Lidskii [5]. In these papers measurement of ξ^j is permitted. Other interesting work on stochastic optimal control has appeared in Drenick and Shaw [6], Florentine [7], Fel'dbaum [8], and Wonham [9]. For an analysis of some characteristics of functions of a Markov process see Rosenblatt [10].

Bibliography

1. N. N. Krasovskii, "On Optimal Control in the Presence of Random Disturbances," *Applied Mathematics and Mechanics*, Vol. 24, No. 1, pp. 82–102 (January 1960).
2. I. Ia. Katz, and N. N. Krasovskii, "On the Stability of Systems with Random Parameters," *Applied Mathematics and Mechanics*, Vol. 24, No. 5, pp. 809–823 (September 1960).
3. N. N. Krasovskii, and E. A. Lidskii, "Analytical Design of Controllers in Systems with Random Attributes," *Automation and Remote Control*, Vol. 22, No. 9, 10, and 11, pp. 1021–1025, 1191–1146, and 1289–1294 (September, October, and November 1961).
4. N. N. Krasovskii, and E. A. Lidskii, "Analytical Design of Controllers in Stochastic Systems with Velocity Limited Controlling Action," *Applied Mathematics and Mechanics*, Vol. 25, No. 3, pp. 627–693 (May 1961).
5. E. A. Lidskii, "On the Analytical Design of Controllers in Systems with Random Characteristics," *Applied Mathematics and Mechanics*, Vol. 26, No. 2, pp. 373–383 (March 1962).
6. R. F. Drenick, and L. Shaw, "Optimal Control of Linear Plants with Random Parameters," *IEEE Trans. on Automatic Control*, Vol. AC-9, pp. 236–244 (July 1964).
7. J. J. Florentine, "Optimal Control of Continuous Time, Markov, Stochastic Systems," *Journal of Electronics and Control*, Vol. 10, pp. 473–481 (October 1961).
8. A. A. Fel'dbaum, "On the Optimal Control of Markov Objects," *Automation and Remote Control*, Vol. 23, No. 8, pp. 927–941 (February 1962).
9. W. M. Wonham, "Stochastic Problems in Optimal Control," *RIAS Technical Report* 63-14, 1963.
10. M. Rosenblatt, "Functions of a Markov Process that are Markovian," *Journal of Mathematics and Mechanics*, Vol. 8, No. 4, pp. 585–596 (August 1959).

CHAPTER 6

Suboptimal Adaptive Control Systems

1. Introduction

In the previous chapter Eq. (4.16) was used to derive a control policy which was labeled "optimal" for the specific plant and criterion function. This example serves to illustrate the difficulties which sometimes appear in formulating precisely what is sought in an adaptive control problem. For the specific system chosen we were able to obtain an explicit closed-form solution for the optimal control policy. This result perhaps conceals the underlying computational difficulties which may arise when one is analyzing systems of this type. Even for very simple systems, analytical obstacles may be encountered which make the evaluation of the optimal control rule very difficult, if not impossible.

In order to provide an example of the problems related to the determination of a Bayes control policy associated with a simple system, we will analyze a system in which the plant is described by a linear scalar difference equation with an unknown coefficient. The controller has available to it the record of the past control inputs. It will be assumed that the state of the system is measured through a channel which contains additive noise. The engineer must select a control policy in Γ^* which minimizes the Bayes cost with respect to a specific *a priori* distribution for the unknown parameter.

Although the problem as posed is conceptually quite simple, the explicit determination of the desired Bayes policy is quite difficult. This leads the control system designer to search for a control rule which approximates the Bayes policy in some sense, and which may be computed in a practical manner. Observe that the fundamental difficulties encountered in synthesis of adaptive system controllers are occasioned by the fact that the domain of H is $\Gamma^* \times \Theta^*$ rather than only Γ^*. One possible way to circumvent this obstacle is to make an estimate of the true value of θ from the observable data, $\hat{\theta}(z_j)$. Then $\bar{u}$ is selected to minimize $H(\bar{u}, \hat{\theta})$. The estimation of θ is frequently termed the identification problem, and the subsequent minimization is termed optimization. A configuration in which the "best" estimator is used in conjunction with the optimal control rule based upon this estimate has been referred to as an "ideal adaptive" system. In general we would not expect that such a configuration would be optimal but it has been asserted that if the plant is linear and if the performance functional is quadratic the operations of identification and optimization can be performed separately.

There are other suboptimal policies which can be deduced by examination of the recurrence formula which the Bayes rules must satisfy [Eq. (4.16)]. These suboptimal policies do not have the intuitive attraction of an "ideal adaptive" policy, but we will provide the results of a simulation study which will show that the latter policies have a smaller Bayes cost than does a control which separates identification and optimization.

2. Mathematical Formulation

The fixed element of the control system will be described by the scalar difference equation:

$$\begin{aligned} x_{j+1} &= ax_j + \xi v_j, \qquad 0 \leqslant j \leqslant N-1, \\ x_0 &= x(0). \end{aligned} \tag{6.1}$$

As before, x_j is the system state at time $t = j\Delta$ and v_j is the scalar control force at time $t = j\Delta$. We will assume that (see Definition 2.1)

$$V_j = E_1, \qquad j = 0, ..., N.$$

The problem to be solved is the classical regulator problem in which the control sequence v^N is chosen to drive the state of the system toward the origin in state space. The quality of performance of the compensation is measured by the functional

$$h(x^N, \bar{v}) = \sum_{i=0}^{N} x_i^2 + v_N^2. \tag{6.2}$$

Before the problem can be investigated in a meaningful fashion, we must specify both the *a priori* knowledge available to the control system designer, and the information which becomes available to him as the process evolves in time. Consider first the *a priori* information. It will be assumed that Eq. (6.1) and the value of the parameter a are known. It is also known that

$$\begin{aligned} \mathrm{Prob}(\xi \leqslant \omega) &= 0, \qquad \omega < \theta, \\ &= 1, \qquad \omega \geqslant \theta. \end{aligned}$$

The parameter set Θ contains two elements:

$$\Theta = \{\theta_1, \theta_2\}.$$

The scalars θ_1 and θ_2 are both assumed to be nonzero. It is also known that the true value of the parameter θ will be chosen by a random mechanism is such a way that

$$\mathrm{Prob}(\theta = \theta_1) = p > 0$$

and

$$\mathrm{Prob}(\theta = \theta_2) = q > 0 \tag{6.3}$$

where $p + q = 1$.

As the process unfolds in time, the controller has available to it two time sequences. On the one hand, the sequence of past plant inputs, v^{j-1}, is observed. The system state is not measurable directly by the controller. Instead, the controller measures y^j, where the sequence y^j is generated by the equation

$$y_j = x_j + \eta_j \, . \tag{6.4}$$

The vector η^N is composed of a sequence of independent random scalars, each component of which is chosen from a population with distribution function $\mathrm{Nor}(0, {\sigma_1}^2)$, where ${\sigma_1}^2$ is a constant that is known to the designer.

On the basis of the data described above, the engineer seeks to choose a control strategy $v^* \in \Gamma^*$ in such a way that the Bayes cost of the process is minimized. Since Γ is essentially complete for a Bayes ordering of Γ^*, we may restrict attention to pure control policies without loss of generality. It is interesting to note that if $\sigma_1 = 0$, the observation vector contains sufficient information to enable the controller to evaluate θ directly at time $t = \Delta$. Thus, the case in which there is no noise in the state measurement admits of a rather trivial solution.

3. A Nonadaptive Control Problem

Before investigating the problem posed in Section 2, let us analyze the situation in which θ is known at the beginning of the process; that is, we will consider the case where $\Theta = \{\theta_1\}$. This problem can be solved quite simply using the following dynamic programming argument. Define the following minimum cost functional:

$$\begin{aligned} J(\bar{v}, k) &= \min_{\bar{v} \in \Gamma} E\left\{ \sum_{i=k+1}^{N} x_i^2 \mid y_k \right\} \\ &= \min_{\bar{v} \in \Gamma} E\{x_{k+1}^2 \mid y_k\} + E\left\{ \sum_{i=k+2}^{N} x_i^2 \mid y_k \right\}. \end{aligned}$$

By the definition of the conditional expectation operator,

$$\begin{aligned} E\left\{ \sum_{i=k+2}^{N} x_i^2 \mid y_k \right\} &= E\left\{ E\left\{ \sum_{i=k+2}^{N} x_i^2 \mid y_{k+1} \right\} \mid y_k \right\} \\ &= E\{J(\bar{v}, k+1) \mid y_k\}. \end{aligned}$$

If it is assumed

$$J(\bar{v}, k) = P_k y_k^2 + Q_k ,$$

then

$$\begin{aligned} P_k y_k^2 + Q_k &= \min_{\bar{v} \in \Gamma} E\{(a x_k + \theta_1 v_k)^2 + P_{k+1}(a x_k + \theta_1 v_k + \eta_{k+1})^2 + Q_{k+1} \mid y_k\} \\ &= \min_{\bar{v} \in \Gamma} E\{(a y_k + \theta_1 v_k - a\eta_k)^2 + P_{k+1}(a y_k + \theta_1 v_k + \eta_{k+1} - a\eta_k)^2 \\ &\quad + Q_{k+1} \mid y_k\} \\ &= \min_{\bar{v} \in \Gamma} E\{(P_{k+1} + 1)(a y_k + \theta_1 v_k)^2 \mid y_k\} + a^2\sigma_1^2(P_{k+1} + 1) \\ &\quad + \sigma^2 P_{k+1} + Q_{k+1} . \end{aligned}$$

If the optimal $\bar{v} \in \Gamma$ is defined to be $\bar{u}$, we see that

$$\bar{u}_k = -\frac{ay_k}{\theta_1}. \tag{6.5}$$

Note also that

$$\begin{aligned} P_k &= 1, \qquad k = N, \\ &= 0, \qquad k < N. \end{aligned}$$

The solution to this problem has some rather interesting properties. In the first place, the identification is independent of optimization in the sense that x_j is estimated from the observed data, and then this estimate is substituted into the expression for the control rule which would be used if the actual value of x_j were known.

This example also displays another characteristic of the non-adaptive control problem. Except for the terminal stage of the control process, the expected cost of the optimal control is independent of the state of the system. As a result of this, one obtains the same optimal control policy and the same minimum cost if the problem is formulated as a sequence of single-stage optimization problems. In other words, if we simply minimize the expected value of the incremental cost at each stage of the process, the optimal control policy for the criterion functional given in Eq. (6.2) will be obtained.

4. Derivation of the Bayes Policy

For the problem posed in Section 2, we will find it convenient to place the recurrence formula which the Bayes policy must satisfy in a form which is slightly different from that which was obtained in Chapter 4 where measurement of ξ^N was permitted. If at time $t = s\Delta$, the values of v^s, y^s, and θ were known, then the expected value of the incremental cost would be

$$r_s = E\{W_s \mid v^s, y^s, \theta\}.$$

From Eq. (6.2) it is evident that $W_s = x_s^2$ for all $s < N$. Consequently,

$$r_s = \int x_s^2 p(x_s \mid v^s, y^s, \theta)\, d(\Omega x_s), \qquad s \neq N.$$

But the values of v^s, y^s, and θ are not known at the beginning of the process, so we define the expected value of the incremental cost as follows:

$$R_s = E(r_s\}$$
$$= \int W_s p(x_s \mid v^s, y^s, \theta) p(v^s, y^s, \theta)\, d\Omega(x_s, y^s, v^s, \theta).$$

Expanding the joint probability density function as a product of conditional densities we find that

$$p(v^s, y^s, \theta) = p(v^s, y^s) p(\theta \mid v^s, y^s).$$

From Eq. (6.4) it is apparent that $p(x_s \mid v^s, y^s, \theta) = p(x_s \mid y_s)$, and therefore,

$$R_s = \int W_s p(x_s \mid y_s) p(v^s, y^s) p(\theta \mid v^s, y^s) p d\Omega(x_s, y^s, v^s, \theta).$$

From the Bayes formula we obtain

$$p(\theta \mid v^s, y^s) = \frac{p(v^s, y^s \mid \theta) p_0(\theta)}{p(v^s, y^s)}.$$

Thus, the following relation ensues:

$$R_s = \int W_s p(x_s \mid y_s) p(v^s, y^s \mid \theta) p_0(\theta)\, d\Omega(x_s, y^s, v^s, \theta).$$

Just as in the derivation of Eq. (4.8), one can show that

$$p(v^s, y^s \mid \theta) = \prod_{i=0}^{s} p(v_i \mid v^{i-1}, y^i) \prod_{i=0}^{s} p(y_i \mid y^{i-1}, v^{i-1}, \theta).$$

Placing this expression into the equation for R_s gives

$$R_s = \int W_s p(x_s \mid y_s) \prod_{i=0}^{s} p(v_i \mid v^{i-1}, y^i) \prod_{i=0}^{s} p(y_i \mid y^{i-1}, v^{i-1}, \theta)$$
$$\times\, p_0(\theta)\, d\Omega(x_s, y^s, v^s, \theta).$$

Our approach to the solution of this optimization problem is exactly like that presented in Eq. (4.16).

We define

$$\alpha_s = \int W_s p(x_s \mid y_s) \prod_{i=0}^{s} p(y_i \mid y^{i-1}, v^{i-1}, \theta) p_0(\theta)\, d\Omega(x_s, \theta);$$

$$\beta_s = \prod_{i=0}^{s} p(v_i \mid v^{i-1}, y^i).$$

The problem is now in precisely the same form which was derived in Chapter 4. Hence, we need only evaluate the sequence ρ^N in order to determine the Bayes control policy. To do this let us first determine the probability density functions in the above equations. From Eq. (6.4) we see that

$$y_s - x_s = \eta_s,$$

and therefore,

$$p(x_s \mid y_s) = \frac{1}{\sqrt{2\pi}\sigma_1} \exp\left\{ - \frac{(x_s - y_s)^2}{2\sigma_1^2} \right\}. \tag{6.6}$$

From Eq. (6.1) we see that

$$y_{s+1} - \eta_{s+1} = a y_s + \theta v_s - a\eta_s,$$

or

$$y_{s+1} - a y_s - \theta v_s = \eta_{s+1} - a\eta_s.$$

Using the addition formula for independent Gaussian random variables, it can be shown that $(\eta_{s+1} - a\eta_s)$ has a normal probability distribution function, Nor$(0, (1 + a^2)\sigma_1^2)$. Let us define

$$(1 + a^2)\sigma_1^2 = \sigma^2.$$

Then

$$\prod_{i=1}^{s} p(y_i \mid y_{i-1}, v_{i-1}, \theta) = \left(\frac{1}{\sqrt{2\pi}\sigma} \right)^s \exp\left\{ - \frac{1}{2\sigma^2} \sum_{i=1}^{s} (y_i - a y_{i-1} - \theta v_{i-1})^2 \right\}. \tag{6.7}$$

Accordingly, on combining Eqs. (6.3) and (6.7), we obtain

$$\int \prod_{i=1}^{s} p(y_i \mid y_{i-1}, v_i, \theta) p_0(\theta)\, d\Omega(\theta)$$
$$= \left(\frac{1}{\sqrt{2\pi}\sigma} \right)^s \left[p \exp\left\{ - \frac{1}{2\sigma^2} \sum_{i=1}^{s} (y_i - a y_{i-1} - \theta_1 v_{i-1})^2 \right\} \right. \tag{6.8}$$
$$\left. + q \exp\left\{ - \frac{1}{2\sigma^2} \sum_{i=1}^{s} (y_i - a y_{i-1} - \theta_2 v_{i-1})^2 \right\} \right].$$

For notational convenience, let us define the following function:

$$\Sigma_k^j = \left[\exp\left\{-\frac{1}{2\sigma^2}\sum_{i=1}^{j}(y_i - ay_{i-1} - \theta_k v_{i-1})^2\right\}\right]\delta(y_0 - y(0)). \quad (6.9)$$

Then, Eq. (6.8) can be written in the form

$$\int \prod_{i=0}^{s} p(y_i \mid y_{i-1}, v_i, \theta)p_0(\theta)\, d\Omega(\theta) = \left(\frac{1}{\sqrt{2\pi}\sigma}\right)^s [p\Sigma_1^s + q\Sigma_2^s]. \quad (6.10)$$

Substituting Eqs. (6.10) and (6.6) into Eq. (6.5), we have

$$\alpha_s = \int W_s \left[\frac{1}{\sqrt{2\pi}\sigma_1}\exp\left\{-\frac{(x_s - y_s)^2}{2\sigma_1^2}\right\}\right]\left(\frac{1}{\sqrt{2\pi}\sigma}\right)^s [p\Sigma_1^s + q\Sigma_2^s]\, d\Omega(x_s). \quad (6.11)$$

With the explicit expression for α_s given above we may now use Eq. (4.16) to obtain the Bayes policy. To minimize α_N we must choose $\bar{v}_N \equiv 0$. Setting $v_N = 0$ in Eq. (6.11) yields

$$\begin{aligned}\rho_N &= \inf_{\bar{v}_N} \alpha_N \\ &= \int x_N^2 \left[\frac{1}{\sqrt{2\pi}\sigma_1}\exp\left\{-\frac{(x_N - y_N)^2}{2\sigma_1^2}\right\}\right]\left(\frac{1}{\sqrt{2\pi}\sigma}\right)^N [p\Sigma_1^N + q\Sigma_2^N]\, d\Omega(x_N).\end{aligned}$$

If the indicated integration is performed, it follows that

$$\rho_N = \left(\frac{1}{\sqrt{2\pi}\sigma}\right)^N (\sigma_1^2 + y_N^2)[p\Sigma_1^N + q\Sigma_2^N]. \quad (6.12)$$

By definition,

$$\rho_{N-1} = \inf_{\bar{v}_{N-1}} \left[\alpha_{N-1} + \int \rho_N\, d\Omega(y_N)\right].$$

The function Σ_i^N can be expanded by factoring out Σ_i^{N-1} to obtain

$$\begin{aligned}\int \rho_N\, d\Omega(y_N) = \left(\frac{1}{\sqrt{2\pi}\sigma}\right)^N \Bigg[& p\Sigma_1^{N-1}\int_{-\infty}^{\infty}(\sigma_1^2 + y_N^2) \\ &\times \exp\left\{-\frac{1}{2\sigma^2}(y_N - ay_{N-1} - \theta_1 v_{N-1})^2\right\} dy_N \\ &+ q\Sigma_2^{N-1}\int_{-\infty}^{\infty}(\sigma_1^2 + y_N^2) \\ &\times \exp\left\{-\frac{1}{2\sigma^2}(y_N - ay_{N-1} - \theta_2 v_{N-1})^2\right\} dy_N\Bigg],\end{aligned}$$

or

$$\int \rho_N \, d\Omega(y_N) = \Big[p\Sigma_1^{N-1}({\sigma_1}^2 + \sigma^2 + (ay_{N-1} + \theta_1 v_{N-1})^2)$$

$$+ q\Sigma_1^{N-1}({\sigma_1}^2 + \sigma^2 + (ay_{N-1} + \theta_2 v_{N-1})^2)\Big]\left(\frac{1}{\sqrt{2\pi\sigma}}\right)^{N-1}. \tag{6.13}$$

From Eqs. (6.11) and (6.12) it is clear that

$$\alpha_{N-1} = ({\sigma_1}^2 + y_{N-1}^2)\left(\frac{1}{\sqrt{2\pi\sigma}}\right)^{N-1}[p\Sigma_2^{N-1} + q\Sigma_2^{N-1}],$$

and therefore,

$$\rho_{N-1} = \inf_{\bar{v}_{N-1}} \left(\frac{1}{\sqrt{2\pi\sigma}}\right)^{N-1} [(2{\sigma_1}^2 + \sigma^2 + y_{N-1}^2 + (ay_{N-1} + \theta_1 v_{N-1})^2)p\Sigma_1^{N-1}$$

$$+ (2{\sigma_1}^2 + \sigma^2 + y_{N-1}^2 + (ay_{N-1} + \theta_2 v_{N-1})^2)q\Sigma_2^{N-1}].$$

To minimize this expression we differentiate the bracketed term with respect to v_{N-1} to obtain a relation that the optimal control rule must satisfy.

$$\theta_1(ay_{N-1} + \theta_1 v_{N-1})p\Sigma_1^{N-1} + \theta_2(ay_{N-1} + \theta_2 v_{N-1})q\Sigma_2^{N-1} = 0.$$

Solving the above equation for $\bar{v}_{N-1}$, we find

$$(\bar{v}_{N-1})_{\min} = -ay_{N-1}\frac{[\theta_1 p\Sigma_1^{N-1} + \theta_2 q\Sigma_2^{N-1}]}{p{\theta_1}^2\Sigma_1^{N-1} + q{\theta_2}^2\Sigma_2^{N-1}}. \tag{6.14}$$

If Eq. (6.14) is substituted into the expression for ρ_{N-1}, the following result is obtained (see Appendix G):

$$\rho_{N-1} = \left(\frac{1}{\sqrt{2\pi\sigma}}\right)^{N-1}\Big[(2{\sigma_1}^2 + \sigma^2 + y_{N-1}^2)p\Sigma_1^{N-1} + (2{\sigma_1}^2 + \sigma^2 + y_{N-1}^2)q\Sigma_2^{N-1}$$

$$+ a^2y_{N-1}^2\frac{pq(\theta_2 - \theta_1)^2\Sigma_1^{N-1}\Sigma_2^{N-1}}{{\theta_1}^2p\Sigma_1^{N-1} + {\theta_2}^2q\Sigma_2^{N-1}}\Big]. \tag{6.15}$$

Thus far, the procedure for evaluating the Bayes control policy has met with success. In Eq. (6.14) the $(N-1)$st component of the Bayes policy is given explicitly and Eq. (6.15) is a measure of the expected cost of the remaining stages of the process. Unfortunately, solution of the recurrence formula now becomes more difficult. To see why this is so, one must return to Eq. (6.12). The decomposition property of Σ_i^N permitted $\int \rho_N \, d\Omega(y_N)$ to be written as a sum of terms consisting of a Σ_i^{N-1} factor and a Gaussian variance type integral. The quantity ρ_{N-1}, however, does not have this linearity property and $\int \rho_{N-1} \, d\Omega(y_{N-1})$ cannot be written in terms of known special functions. Thus, the Bayes control policy for this process cannot be directly determined by use of the recurrence formula for the ρ_j.

This anomaly should not cause too much surprise. Even in nonadaptive problems, only those which investigate the control of a linear plant with a quadratic criterion of performance seem amenable to direct analytical solution. The difficulty with the adaptive control problem formulated in this chapter is intimately connected with the fact that for all $j < N$, ρ_j is not a quadratic function of y_j, and consequently, the cost of gathering information and of estimating the unknown parameter cannot be expressed directly in terms of known special functions.

5. Two Suboptimal Policies

In the previous section of this chapter the method derived in Chapter 4 was applied in an attempt to evaluate a Bayes control policy for this adaptive problem. We were not successful in this endeavor because of the complexity of the recurrence formula which ρ_j must satisfy. Since the Bayes policy is so difficult to determine, one might instead seek a control policy which has a relatively small Bayes cost, and which can be computed directly. In this section we will derive two suboptimal control policies which are closely related to the Bayes rule for the problem.

Let us analyze the simplest of these suboptimal control rules first. In Section 3, a nonadaptive version of this control problem was considered, and it was shown that the control rule which minimizes $\sum_{i=0}^{N} x_i^2 + v_N^2$ was almost surely equal to the policy which minimizes the expected value of x_{i+1}^2 at time $t = i\Delta$; that is, the problem could be viewed as a sequence of single-stage optimal control problems. If this idea is applied to the adaptive situation, we might seek to minimize

$E\{x_{i+1}^2\}$ by employing all available data at time $t = i\Delta$. This problem has already been solved because $\bar{u}_{N-1}$ is the Bayes control for a one-stage process of this type. Thus, this suboptimal control is given by [cf. Eq. (6.14)]

$$\begin{aligned} \bar{w} &= -ay_j \frac{\theta_1 p \Sigma_1{}^j + \theta_2 q \Sigma_2{}^j}{p\theta_1{}^2 \Sigma_1{}^j + \theta_2{}^2 q \Sigma_2{}^j}, \qquad && j = 0, ..., N-1, \\ &= 0, && j = N. \end{aligned} \tag{6.16}$$

It is interesting to consider the structure of this control policy in some detail. Let us define

$$\tilde{\theta} = \frac{p\theta_1{}^2 \Sigma_1{}^j + q\theta_2{}^2 \Sigma_2{}^j}{p\theta_1 \Sigma_1{}^j + q\theta_2 \Sigma_2{}^j}. \tag{6.17}$$

It is clear that $\tilde{\theta}$ is an estimate of the true value of θ. For example, if θ_1 is the true value of θ, then

$$\lim_{j\to\infty} E\left\{\frac{\Sigma_2{}^j}{\Sigma_1{}^j}\right\} = 0,$$

and we see that, in this case,

$$\lim_{j\to\infty} E\{\tilde{\theta}\} = \theta_1 .$$

In fact, as more information is acquired about the plant characteristics, $\tilde{\theta}$ converges in probability to the true value of the parameter θ. The control rule $\bar{w}$, therefore, estimates θ using Eq. (6.17) and then uses the optimal nonadaptive control policy for this choice of $\tilde{\theta}$. Note two things about this policy. First, this choice of θ is a poor one in the sense that the probability that the true value of θ is $\tilde{\theta}$ is zero for all j. Second, no weight has been given to the effect of the different amounts of learning which one might obtain with different control policies.

To make this idea of "different amounts of learning for different control policies" more precise, let us turn to the second of the suboptimal control policies. From the preceding discussion, we see that the form of the last term in Eq. (6.15) made it impossible to continue the explicit solution of the recurrence formula for the Bayes control policy. In order to circumvent this difficulty consider the following heuristic argument. At any given time $t = j\Delta$ in the control process the control element will behave as though one of the following three statements is true:

(1) θ_1 is much more likely than θ_2.
(2) θ_2 is much more likely than θ_1.
(3) θ_1 and θ_2 are about equally likely.

There are, of course, regions which separate each of the adjacent zones of the above classification in which the state of knowledge is difficult to categorize but this effect will be neglected for the present. For example, one might begin the control process with *a priori* information which indicated that θ_1 and θ_2 were about equally likely. As the process unfolds and as more data are available to the control element, it might gradually begin to appear that θ_1 is much more likely than θ_2.

If we assume that the previous statements have been formulated precisely in terms of the observable sequences, v^{j-1} and y^j, these three statements can be viewed as inducing a three-element partition, $\{s_{j1}, s_{j2}, s_{j3}\}$, on the space of observable data at time $t = j\Delta$. It is clear that while the data may fall within a particular element of the partition at time $t = j\Delta$, it may be that at time $t = (j+k)\Delta$ the information will be contained in an element of the partition with a different second subscript. In this control problem we might, for example, have the following sequence of information states: $\{s_{03}, s_{13}, s_{23}, \ldots, s_{81}, s_{91}\}$. This sequence indicates the following character of the example process. During the first few time increments θ_1 and θ_2 appeared equally likely, but toward the end of the control process the controller became fairly certain that the true value of θ was θ_1.

The following difficulty now presents itself. If the observable data is in state s_{ij} at time $t = i\Delta$, what will be the sequence of information states which follow? This sequence of states can never be known exactly because it is a random variable, but a rudimentary dynamic programming argument indicates that the optimal $\bar{v}_j$ depends upon the probabilities of the various sequences. Calculating the probability that the observation vector $z_j \in s_{jk}$, $j > i$ conditioned on $z_i \in s_{ir}$, would be as difficult as solving the optimization problem directly. Consequently, this suboptimal control policy will be calculated on the premise that if $z_i \in s_{ik}$, then $z_j \in s_{jk}$ for $j > i$. This is a natural supposition if $z_i \in s_{i1}$ or s_{i2} but if θ_1 and θ_2 equally likely at $t = i\Delta$, we would not expect this state to persist. In this circumstance the postulate can be regarded as a bias restriction.

The foregoing discussion has provided an informal analysis of the relative state of the information available to the controller at a given time. Let us make the representation of the data more precise. We were unable to evaluate the Bayes control policy because the integral of the last term of Eq. (6.15) could not be written in terms of known special functions. Let us assume that ρ_{N-j} has been reduced to the form

$$\rho_{N-j} = \left(\frac{1}{\sqrt{2\pi}\sigma}\right)^{N-j} [(\sigma_{3,N-j}^2 + a_{N-j}y_{N-j}^2)p\Sigma_1^{N-j} + (\sigma_{4,N-j}^2 + b_{N-j}y_{N-j}^2)q\Sigma_2^{N-j}]. \tag{6.18}$$

Note that ρ_N has this form with

$$\sigma_{3,N}^2 = \sigma^2, \qquad \sigma_{4,N} = \sigma^2, \qquad a_N = 1, \qquad b_N = 1. \tag{6.19}$$

It is shown in Appendix H that if Eq. (6.18) is valid, then the optimal $\bar{v}_{N-j-1}$ is given by

$$(\bar{v}_{N-j-1})_{\min} = -ay_{N-j-1}\frac{a_{N-j}\theta_1 p\Sigma_1^{N-j-1} + b_{N-j}\theta_2 q\Sigma_2^{N-j-1}}{a_{N-j}\theta_1{}^2 p\Sigma_1^{N-j-1} + b_{N-j}\theta_2{}^2 q\Sigma_2^{N-j-1}}. \tag{6.20}$$

Unfortunately, the form of ρ_{N-j} given by Eq. (6.18) does not recur in ρ_{N-j-1}. This characteristic of the ρ's was seen in the transformation from ρ_N to ρ_{N-1}. It is shown in Appendix G that if ρ_{N-j} is given by Eq. (6.18), we can write

$$\rho_{N-j-1} = \left(\frac{1}{\sqrt{2\pi}\sigma}\right)^{N-j-1} [(\sigma_{3,N-j-1}^2 + a_{N-j-1}y_{N-j-1}^2)p\Sigma_1^{N-j-1} + (\sigma_{4,N-j-1}^2 + b_{N-j-1}y_{N-j-1}^2)q\Sigma_2^{N-j-1}] + \epsilon,$$

where (1) if

$$\gamma_{N-j} = \frac{a_{N-j}\theta_1{}^2 p\Sigma_1^{N-j-1}}{b_{N-j}\theta_2{}^2 q\Sigma_1^{N-j-1}} > 1,$$

then

$$a_{N-j-1} = 1,$$

$$b_{N-j-1} = 1 + \frac{a^2 b_{N-j}(\theta_2 - \theta_1)^2}{\theta_1^2},$$

and

$$\epsilon = \left(\frac{1}{\sqrt{2\pi\sigma}}\right)^{N-j-1} qb_{N-j}\Sigma_2^{N-j-1} \frac{(\theta_2 - \theta_1)^2}{\theta_1^2} \frac{1}{\gamma_{N-j}} + O\left(\frac{1}{\gamma_{N-j}^2}\right); \tag{6.21}$$

(2) if $\gamma_{N-j} < 1$, then

$$a_{N-j-1} = 1 + \frac{a^2 a_{N-j}(\theta_2 - \theta_1)^2}{\theta_2^2},$$

$$b_{N-j-1} = 1,$$

and

$$\epsilon = \left(\frac{1}{\sqrt{2\pi\sigma}}\right)^{N-j-1} pa_{N-j}\Sigma_1^{N-j-1} \frac{(\theta_2 - \theta_1)^2}{\theta_2^2} \gamma_{N-j} + O(\gamma_{N-j}^2); \tag{6.22}$$

(3) if $\gamma_{N-j} \simeq 1$, then

$$a_{N-j-1} = 1 + \frac{(\theta_2 - \theta_1)^2}{4\theta_2^2} a_{N-j},$$

$$b_{N-j-1} = 1 + \frac{(\theta_2 - \theta_1)^2}{4\theta_1^2} b_{N-j},$$

and

$$\epsilon = \frac{1}{4}\left(\frac{1}{\sqrt{2\pi\sigma}}\right)^{N-j-1} pa_{N-j}\Sigma_1^{N-j-1} \frac{(\theta_2 - \theta_1)^2}{\theta_2^2} \left(1 - \frac{1}{\gamma_{N-j}}\right)^2 + O\left[\left(1 - \frac{1}{\gamma_{N-j}}\right)^3\right]. \tag{6.23}$$

We can now specify the partition discussed earlier in a more precise manner. It is evident that the classifications related to γ_{N-j} are intimately connected to the partition $\{s_{j1}, s_{j2}, s_{j3}\}$ given before. If the first term in the expansion for the error is taken to be a measure of the ϵ term, then the following division of the space of data available to the controller results:

$$\{v^{j-1}, y^j\} \in s_{j1} \quad \text{if} \quad \frac{qb_{j+1}\Sigma_2^j}{\theta_1^2} \frac{1}{\gamma_{j+1}} \leqslant \frac{pa_{j+1}\Sigma_1^j}{\theta_2^2} \gamma_{j+1}$$

$$\text{and} \quad \frac{qb_{j+1}\Sigma_2^j}{\theta_1^2} \frac{1}{\gamma_{j+1}} \leqslant \frac{pa_{j+1}\Sigma_1^j}{4\theta_2^2} \left(1 - \frac{1}{\gamma_{j+1}}\right)^2; \tag{6.24}$$

$$\{v^{j-1}, y^i\} \in s_{j2} \quad \text{if} \quad \frac{pa_{j+1}\Sigma_1{}^j}{\theta_2{}^2}\gamma_{j+1} < \frac{qb_{j+1}\Sigma_2{}^j}{\theta_1{}^2}\frac{1}{\gamma_{j+1}}$$

$$\text{and} \qquad \gamma_{j+1} \leqslant \frac{1}{4}\left(1 - \frac{1}{\gamma_{j+1}}\right)^2;$$

and (6.24 cont.)

$$\{v^{j-1}, y^i\} \in s_{j3} \quad \text{if} \quad \frac{pa_{j+1}\Sigma_1{}^j\left(1 - \dfrac{1}{\gamma_{N-j}}\right)^2}{4\theta_2{}^2} < \frac{qb_{j+1}\Sigma_2{}^j}{\theta_1{}^2}\frac{1}{\gamma_{j+1}}$$

$$\text{and} \qquad \frac{1}{4}\left(1 - \frac{1}{\gamma_{j+1}}\right)^2 < \gamma_{j+1}\,.$$

The above relations are not yet a partition since they contain the factors a_{j+1} and b_{j+1} which are implicitly functions of future data. At this point we introduce the hypothesis that if $\{v^{j-1}, y^j\} \in s_{jk}$, we will select $\bar{v}_j$ as if $\{v^{i-1}, y^i\} \in s_{ik}$ for all $i > j$.

To see the implication of this hypothesis return to the recurrence relations given by Eqs. (6.21), (6.22), and (6.23). Define the following parameters:

$$\begin{aligned}
a^0_{N-j-1} &= 1,\\
b^0_{N-j-1} &= 1 + \frac{a^2 b^0_{N-j}(\theta_2 - \theta_1)^2}{\theta_1{}^2},\\
a^1_{N-j-1} &= 1 + \frac{a^2 a^1_{N-j}(\theta_2 - \theta_1)^2}{\theta_2{}^2},\\
b^1_{N-j-1} &= 1,\\
a^{(2)}_{N-j-1} &= 1 + a^2\frac{(\theta_2 - \theta_1)^2}{4\theta_2{}^2}a^{(2)}_{N-j},\\
b^{(2)}_{N-j-1} &= 1 + a^2\frac{(\theta_2 - \theta_1)^2}{4\theta_1{}^2}b^{(2)}_{N-j},
\end{aligned} \tag{6.25}$$

and

$$a_N{}^0 = b_N{}^0 = a_N{}^1 = b_N{}^1 = a_N{}^2 = b_N{}^2 = 1.$$

Solving this set of difference equations for $a_i{}^j$ and $b_i{}^j$, we obtain

$$\begin{aligned}
a^0_{N-j} &= 1,\\
b^0_{N-j} &= \frac{1 - [a^2(\theta_2 - \theta_1)^2/\theta_1{}^2]^j}{1 - [a^2(\theta_2 - \theta_1)^2/\theta_1{}^2]},
\end{aligned} \tag{6.26}$$

$$a_{N-j}^{1} = \frac{1 - [a^2(\theta_2 - \theta_1)^2/\theta_2{}^2]^j}{1 - [a^2(\theta_2 - \theta_1)^2/\theta_2{}^2]},$$

$$b_{N-j}^{1} = 1,$$

$$a_{N-j}^{(2)} = \frac{1 - [a^2(\theta_2 - \theta_1)^2/4\theta_2{}^2]^j}{1 - [a^2(\theta_2 - \theta_1)^2/4\theta_2{}^2]}, \qquad (6.26\ \text{cont.})$$

$$b_{N-j}^{(2)} = \frac{1 - [a^2(\theta_2 - \theta_1)^2/4\theta_1]^j}{1 - [a^2(\theta_2 - \theta_1)^2/4\theta_1{}^2]}.$$

Of course, for certain parameter values the above expressions may not be valid and the appropriate formula for summation of an algebraic series should be used. We now introduce the following partition of the space of plant data:

$$\{v^{j-1}, y^j\} \in s_{j1}' \quad \text{if} \quad \frac{qb_{j+1}^0 \Sigma_2{}^j}{\theta_1{}^2} \frac{1}{\gamma_{j+1}^0} \leqslant \frac{pa_{j+1}^1 \Sigma_1{}^j}{\theta_2{}^2} \gamma_{j+1}^1$$

$$\text{and} \quad \frac{qb_{j+1}^0 \Sigma_2{}^j}{\theta_1{}^2} \frac{1}{\gamma_{j+1}^0} \leqslant \frac{pa_{j+1}^{(2)} \Sigma_1{}^j}{4\theta_2{}^2} \left(1 - \frac{1}{\gamma_{j+1}^{(2)}}\right)^2;$$

$$\{v^{j-1}, y^j\} \in s_{j2}' \quad \text{if} \quad \frac{pa_{j+1}^1 \Sigma_1{}^j \gamma_{j+1}^1}{\theta_2{}^2} < \frac{qb_{j+1}^0 \Sigma_2{}^j}{\theta_1{}^2} \frac{1}{\gamma_{j+1}^0}$$

$$\text{and} \quad a_{j+1}^1 \gamma_{j+1}^1 \leqslant \frac{a_{j+1}^{(2)}}{4} \left(1 - \frac{1}{\gamma_{j+1}^{(2)}}\right)^2; \qquad (6.27)$$

and

$$\{v^{j-1}, y^j\} \in s_{j3}' \quad \text{if} \quad \frac{pa_{j+1}^{(2)} \Sigma_1{}^j (1 - 1/\gamma_{j+1}^{(2)})^2}{4\theta_2{}^2} < \frac{qb_{j+1}^0 \Sigma_2{}^j}{\theta_1{}^2} \frac{1}{\gamma_{j+1}^0}$$

$$\text{and} \quad \frac{a_{j+1}^{(2)}}{4} \left(1 - \frac{1}{\gamma_{j+1}^{(2)}}\right)^2 < a_{j+1}^1 \gamma_{j+1}^1;$$

where

$$\gamma_j^{(i)} = \frac{a_j^{(i)} \theta_1{}^2 p \Sigma_1^{j-1}}{b_j^{(i)} \theta_2{}^2 q \Sigma_2^{j-1}}. \qquad (6.28)$$

Then we have the following suboptimal control policy:
If $\{v^{N-j-1}, y^{N-1}\} \in s'_{N-j,k}$, then

$$\bar{v}_{N-j} = -ay_{N-j} \frac{a_{N-j+1}^{(k)} \theta_1 p \Sigma_1^{N-j} + b_{N-j+1}^{(k)} \theta_2 q \Sigma_2^{N-j}}{a_{N-j+1}^{(k)} \theta_1^{\,2} p \Sigma_1^{N-j} + b_{N-j+1}^{(k)} \theta_2^{\,2} q \Sigma_2^{N-j}}, \qquad j \geqslant 1,$$
$$= 0, \qquad j = 0. \tag{6.29}$$

Let us note some properties at this control rule. Define

$$\tilde{\theta}_1 = \frac{a_{N-j+1}^{(k)} \theta_1^{\,2} p \Sigma_1^{N-j} + b_{N-j+1}^{(k)} \theta_2^{\,2} q \Sigma_2^{N-j}}{a_{N-j+1}^{(k)} \theta_1 p \Sigma_1^{N-j} + b_{N-j+1}^{(k)} \theta_2 q \Sigma_2^{N-j}}. \tag{6.30}$$

Then, just as for the control policy given by Eq. (6.16), we have an estimate of θ which converges in probability to the true value of θ. In fact, $\tilde{\theta}_1$ differs from $\tilde{\theta}$ [see Eq. (6.17)] only in the coefficients $a_j^{(i)}$ and $b_j^{(i)}$. We can view the coefficients $a_j^{(k)}$ and $b_j^{(k)}$ as generalized learning coefficients, for it is through these factors that the expected cost of the remaining stages of the process is introduced. They cause the larger of $\{\theta_1, \theta_2\}$ to be favored if θ_1 and θ_2 are about equally likely, but favor the less likely value of θ_i when one value becomes more probable. As the control process approaches its conclusion, the remaining cost declines and, as would be expected, $a_j^{(k)}$ and $b_j^{(k)}$ approach the values necessary for minimizing the incremental cost. We might, therefore, label $\tilde{\theta}_1$, a more "conservative" estimate of θ then $\tilde{\theta}$ was.

6. A Control Policy Using a Best Test for θ

In the previous section, two control policies were derived from an analysis of the recurrence relation which the Bayes policy must satisfy. In both cases the control contained a factor which can be regarded as an estimate of the true value of θ. Both estimates were "poor" in the sense that the probability of either $\tilde{\theta}_1$ or $\tilde{\theta}$ being the correct value of θ is zero. Let us now approach this problem from another point of view. Instead of deriving the suboptimal policy from analysis of the recurrence formula, we will investigate the problem of estimating θ directly. For this purpose we will use the Neyman-Pearson lemma.

Theorem 6.1 (Neyman-Pearson). *Suppose $\Theta = \{\theta_1, \theta_2\}$ and that the information $\{x\}$ is available to the control system designer. If the joint probability density function of the information has the form $f(x \mid \theta)$, then any test of the form*

$$\begin{aligned} \phi(x) &= 1 \qquad &&\text{if } f(x \mid \theta_1) > kf(x \mid \theta_2), \\ &= \gamma(x) &&\text{if } f(x \mid \theta_1) = kf(x \mid \theta_2), \\ &= 0 &&\text{if } f(x \mid \theta_1) < kf(x \mid \theta_2), \end{aligned}$$

for some $k \geqslant 0$ and $0 \leqslant \gamma(x) \leqslant 1$, is best of its size for testing $H_0 : \theta = \theta_2$ against $H_1 : \theta = \theta_1$.

It is not necessary for our purposes to examine in detail the definition of best tests, etc. This theorem simply indicates that if we wish to minimize the probability of choosing θ_2 when θ_1 is correct while maintaining a bound on the probability of choosing θ_1 when θ_2 is correct, then we should use a test of the above form.

From Eq. (6.7),

$$\begin{aligned} &p(y_j, y_{j-1}, ..., y_1 \mid y_0, v^{j-1}, \theta) \\ &\quad = \prod_{i=1}^{j} p(y_i \mid y_{i-1}, v_{i-1}, \theta) \\ &\quad = \left(\frac{1}{\sqrt{2\pi}\sigma}\right)^j \exp\left\{-\frac{1}{2\sigma^2}\sum_{i=1}^{j}(y_i - ay_{i-1} - \theta v_{i-1})^2\right\}. \end{aligned}$$

Since the set on which

$$p(y_j, y_{j-1}, ..., y_1 \mid y_0, v^{j-1}, \theta_1) = p(y_j, y_{j-1}, ..., y_1 \mid y_0, v^{j-1}, \theta_2)$$

if of probability measure zero, we can set $\gamma(x) \equiv 1$ and consider a decision rule of the following form:

At time $t = j\Delta$

$$\text{take } \theta = \theta_1 \qquad \text{if} \quad \frac{\exp\{-(1/2\sigma^2)\sum_{i=1}^{j}(y_i - ay_{i-1} - \theta_1 v_{i-1})^2\}}{\exp\{-(1/2\sigma^2)\sum_{i=1}^{j}(y_i - ay_{i-1} - \theta_2 v_{i-1})^2\}} \geqslant k,$$

$$\text{take } \theta = \theta_2 \qquad \text{if} \quad \frac{\exp\{-(1/2\sigma^2)\sum_{i=1}^{j}(y_i - ay_{i-1} - \theta_1 v_{i-1})^2\}}{\exp\{-(1/2\sigma^2)\sum_{i=1}^{j}(y_i - ay_{i-1} - \theta_2 v_{i-1})^2\}} < k.$$

The concept of a critical region upon which the above test is based does not have the clear meaning in this control problem that it usually has in a hypothesis testing problem. For this reason we will set $k = 1$ and choose the "most likely" value of θ. Thus, our decision rule can be formulated as follows:

At time $t = j\Delta$

$$\begin{aligned}
&\text{take } \theta = \theta_1 \quad \text{if } \sum_{i=1}^{j} (y_i - a y_{i-1} - \theta_1 v_{i-1})^2 \leqslant \sum_{i=1}^{j} (y_i - a y_{i-1} - \theta_2 v_{i-1})^2 \\
&\text{take } \theta = \theta_2 \quad \text{if } \sum_{i=1}^{j} (y_i - a y_{i-1} - \theta_1 v_{i-1})^2 > \sum_{i=1}^{j} (y_i - a y_{i-1} - \theta_2 v_{i-1})^2 .
\end{aligned} \tag{6.31}$$

If this estimate of θ is substituted into the optimal nonadaptive policy given by Eq. (6.5), we obtain the following suboptimal control policy:

$$\begin{aligned}
\bar{v}_j &= -\frac{a y_j}{\theta_1} \quad \text{if } \sum_{i=1}^{j} (y_i - a y_{i-1} - \theta_1 v_{i-1})^2 \leqslant \sum_{i=1}^{j} (y_i - a y_{i-1} - \theta_2 v_{i-1})^2, \quad 0 < j < N, \\
&= -\frac{a y_j}{\theta_2} \quad \text{if } \sum_{i=1}^{j} (y_i - a y_{i-1} - \theta_1 v_{i-1})^2 > \sum_{i=1}^{j} (y_i - a y_{i-1} - \theta_2 v_{i-1})^2, \quad 0 < j < N, \\
&= 0 \quad \text{if } j = N, \\
&= -\frac{a y_0}{\theta_1} \quad \text{if } p > q, \ j = 0, \\
&= -\frac{a y_0}{\theta_2} \quad \text{if } p < q, \ j = 0, \\
&= \begin{cases} \text{Prob}\left(\bar{v}_0 = -\dfrac{a y_0}{\theta_2}\right) = 0.5 \\ \text{Prob}\left(\bar{v}_0 = -\dfrac{a y_0}{\theta_1}\right) = 0.5 \end{cases} \quad \text{if } p = q = 0.5, \ j = 0.
\end{aligned} \tag{6.32}$$

The control rule given by Eq. (6.32) might be characterized as a combination of an optimal estimator and an optimal controller. The resultant control rule is certainly not optimal, since it does not satisfy Eq. (4.16).

7. A Simulation Study

In the preceding work on this problem we have presented three different suboptimal control policies. It is quite difficult to calculate

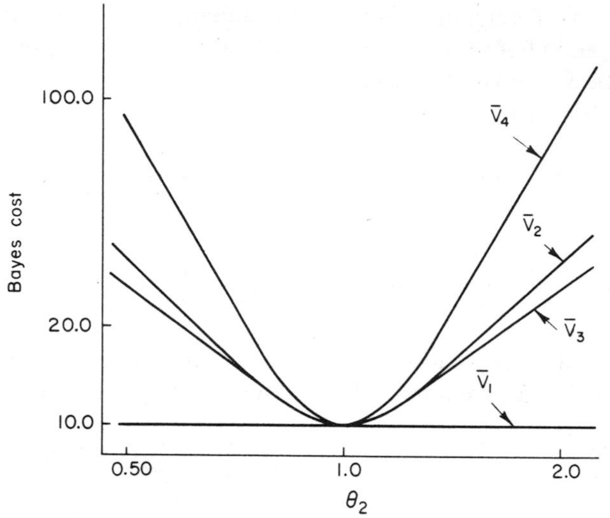

FIG. 6.1. Performance of suboptimal adaptive systems.

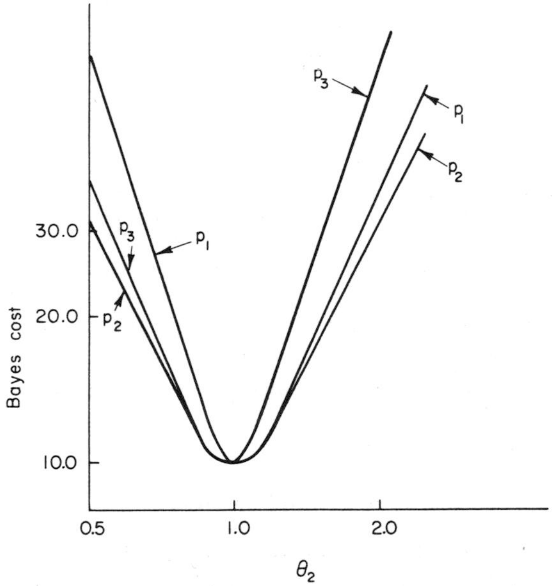

FIG. 6.2. Sensitivity of $H(\bar{v}_2, \theta_0^*)$ to errors in the *a priori* distribution. $p_1 = 0.1, 0.9$; $p_2 = 0.5, 0.5$; $p_3 = 0.9, 0.1$.

the expected cost associated with each policy in closed form because of the complicated structure of the integrals which must be evaluated [see Eq. (H.4)]. For this reason a digital simulation study will be employed to determine the relative performance of the various control policies. The basic format of the simulation study is as follows:

(1) $\theta_1 = 1.0$;
(2) *A priori* $\text{Prob}(\theta = \theta_1) = p = 0.5$;

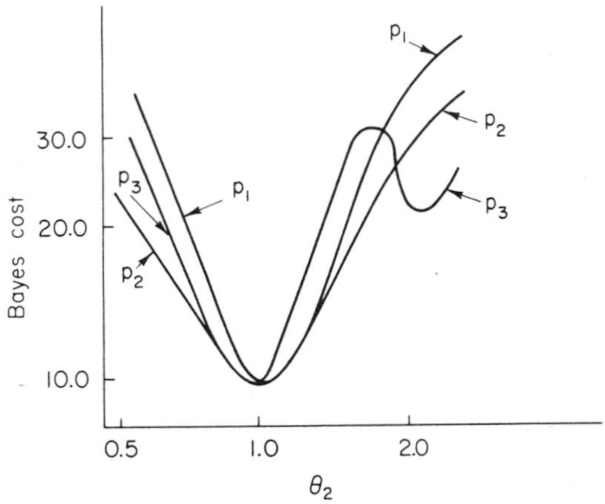

FIG. 6.3. Sensitivity of $H(\bar{v}_3, \theta_0^*)$ to errors in the *a priori* distribution. $p_1 = 0.1$, 0.9; $p_2 = 0.5$, 0.5; $p_3 = 0.9$, 0.1.

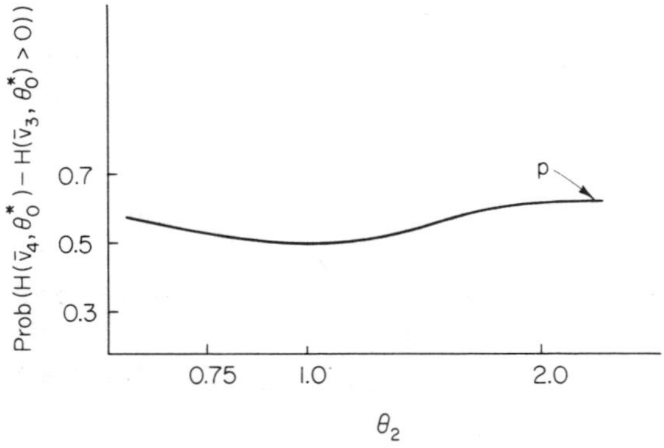

FIG. 6.4. Relative performance of $\bar{v}_4$ and $\bar{v}_3$.

(3) *A priori* Prob($\theta = \theta_2$) $= q = 0.5$;
(3) $N = 10$;
(4) Probability distribution function for x_0 = Nor(0,225);
(5) Probability distribution function for η_i = Nor(0,1);
(6) Number of trials for each value of $\theta_2 = 400$.

Let us denote the true value of θ by $\bar{\theta}$. Then we choose $\bar{\theta} = 1.0$ with probability 1/2, and $\bar{\theta} = \theta_2$ with probability 1/2. Obviously, if we knew $\bar{\theta}$ at the beginning of the control process, we would choose a control rule with a smaller Bayes cost than is possible if we know only Θ. Let us denote a control policy which utilizes knowledge of $\bar{\theta}$ by $\bar{v}_1$. This is, of course, not an adaptive policy, but it gives some information about the amount of performance deterioration due to imperfect knowledge of θ.

The three adaptive policies we wish to compare will be identified as follows:

$\bar{v}_2$, mechanization of Eq. (6.16);
$\bar{v}_3$, mechanization of Eq. (6.29);
$\bar{v}_4$, mechanization of Eq. (6.32).

In Fig. 6.1 the Bayes cost of each of the adaptive control rules is shown for various values of θ_2. We see that in every case the "best" estimate of θ does not lead to the best control. In fact, treating our problem as a sequence of single-stage processes yields better performance than can be obtained using the "best" estimate for $\bar{\theta}$. As might be expected, the control policy which incorporates learning yields superior performance; though, if θ_1 and θ_2 are nearly equal, the difference is slight.

Since the control system designer usually cannot specify the exact $\theta_0{}^* \in \Theta^*$, it is important to study the sensitivity of the performance index to errors in the *a priori* probability distribution. In Figs. 6.2 and 6.3 the system response is measured for systems using $\bar{v}_2$ and $\bar{v}_3$ with various *a priori* probability distributions.

In Fig. 6.1 the three adaptive control policies are compared on the basis of the expected value of the criterion functional. It might be objected that since $\bar{v}_4$ is chosen to maximize the probability of the correct choice of θ, a proper comparison of $\bar{v}_4$ and $\bar{v}_3$ should be based upon Prob$\{[(H(\bar{v}_4, \theta_0{}^*) - H(\bar{v}_3, \theta_0{}^*)] \geqslant 0)\}$. Such a comparison is shown in Fig. 6.4.

8. Conclusion

In this chapter some questions involving the relationship between identification and optimization were investigated by means of an examination of a simple linear system. From this study it should be evident that there exists an intimate interconnection between the system dynamics, the criterion functional, and the manner in which "learning" should be accomplished. In particular, such optimality properties of the identification procedure as "maximal likelihood" are not transmitted to the performance index. Even for the very simple linear system described by Eq. (6.1) the best of the suboptimal controllers used an estimate of θ with no obvious optimality properties [see Eq. (6.30)]. Intuitively, one might suppose that for a single-stage process the *a posteriori* expected value of θ should be used with the optimal nonadaptive controller since there is no "learning" requirement implicit in the selection of the control action. This is not actually the case, however, and the estimate of θ given by Eq. (6.17) is preferable. In fact, since the recurrence formula for the optimal control rule cannot be solved explicitly, it is not obvious that the optimal control for the simple process analyzed here will admit of a decomposition into an estimate of θ and a factor which is linear in the state variable.

The interaction between identification and optimization has been noted at least for nonliner systems by Pearson and it was remarked that the controller need only identify that part of the system dynamics which affects the performance measure. The approach to the adaptive control problem presented in Pearson's work consisted of determining a sequence of control actions which converge to the optimal control action. A difficulty arises if the performance functional is affected by the intermediate behavior of the process, for in this circumstance a large cost may accrue before the control action nears the optimum. For example, each of the three suboptimal control policies derived here converges in probability to the optimal control policy for the case in which the true value of θ is known initially. Yet, the performance indices associated with these policies are significantly different.

Consequently, it should be clear that, even for linear systems with unspecified parameters, the operations of identification and optimization cannot, in general, be separated without regard for the special structure of the control problem. Indeed, it is difficult to specify without detailed analysis what properties of an identification procedure can be regarded as optimal in the control context.

Discussion

SECTION 1. The assertion that the estimation problem can be solved separately from the optimization problem appears in Cox [1]. The phrase "ideal adaptive" control system appeared in Kalman [2].

SECTION 3.
See Bellman [3] and Merriam [4].

SECTION 4. The assumption that the ρ_j is quadratic in y_j appears in Spang [5].

SECTION 6. For a discussion of best tests see Lehmann [6] and Ferguson [7].

SECTION 8. Work on nonlinear adaptive systems appeared in Pearson [8], Pearson and Sarachik [9], and Sarachik [10].

Bibliography

1. H. Cox, "On the Estimation of State Variables and Parameters for Noisy Dynamic Systems," *IEEE Trans. on Automatic Control*, Vol. AC-9, No. 1, pp. 5–12 (January 1964).
2. R. E. Kalman, "Fundamental Study of Adaptive Control Systems," *Technical Report ASD-TR-61-27, RIAS*, Vol. 1, 1962.
3. R. Bellman, *Adaptive Control Processes: A Guided Tour*, Princeton University Press, Princeton, New Jersey, 1961.
4. C. W. Merriam III, *Optimization Theory and the Design of Feedback Control Systems*, McGraw-Hill, New York, 1964.
5. H. A. Spang III, "Optimum Control of an Unknown Linear Plant Using Bayesian Estimation of Error," *Third Symposium on Adaptive Processes*, pp. 27–47, 1964.
6. E. L. Lehmann, *Testing Statistical Hypotheses*, Wiley, New York, 1959.
7. T. Ferguson, unpublished notes, UCLA, 1963.
8. A. E. Pearson, "On Adaptive Optimal Control of Nonlinear Processes," *ASME Journal of Basic Engineering*, Vol. 86, Series D, No. 1, pp. 151–159 (March 1964).
9. A. E. Pearson and P. E. Sarachik, "On the Formulation of Adaptive Optimal Control Problems," Preprints of the 1964 Joint Automatic Control Conference, pp. 13–21, 1964.
10. P. E. Sarachik, "An Approach to the Design of Nonlinear Discrete Self-Optimizing Systems," *Third Symposium on Adaptive Processes*, pp. 128–150, 1964.

CHAPTER 7

Conclusion

In this book some ideas have been presented which will assist the engineer in the solution of certain control system design problems. In particular, we have examined the situation in which not all of the parameters of the plant are initially specified. It should be recalled that one of the fundamental reasons for introducing feedback in any control system is to reduce the sensitivity of the input-output transfer relation to variations in the plant parameters. If it is known that the true value of the unspecified parameter vector lies near some nominal value and if the system performance is insensitive to small variations in these parameters, then the engineer is certainly justified in analyzing the response of a mathematical model employing the nominal parameters. If, however, both of these assumptions are not simultaneously satisfied by the system under consideration, the situation becomes more complex. The index of performance will, in general, depend upon the particular values assumed by the unknown parameters, and therefore, the optimal control for the process will be a function of quantities which are by definition unspecified.

In Chapters 2 and 3 of this book it was shown that the theory of games and statistical decisions forms a natural framework within which the adaptive control problem can be discussed in full generality. Essentially, this follows from associating the game-theoretic definitions with their control system counterparts. An important practical result of this analysis of the structural properties of adaptive processes is a set of sufficient conditions under which Γ is essentially complete (see Theorems 2.2 and 2.4). This is a useful consequence of the theory because the complexity of mechanizing a random control strategy appears to be prohibitive in most applications. The fact that the Bayes cost ordering of Γ^* will, in general, yield a pure optimal control rule should be considered a very desirable attribute of this ordering.

It is interesting to note that optimal nonadaptive control rules are Bayes policies with respect to an initial probability distribution which gives all of its probability measure to one value of $\theta \in \Theta$. Since there exists a nonrandomized Bayes policy under these conditions, one is justified in considering only pure control policies in nonadaptive problems.

In Chapter 4 the theory developed in Chapters 2 and 3 was applied to the adaptive control problem. The recurrence formula given by Eq. (4.16) provides the main tool for evaluating a Bayes control policy. This fundamental functional equation was also derived by Fel'dbaum, but the background of Chapters 2 and 3 permits its application to be extended to a wider class of design situations than Fel'dbaum considered.

In a practical engineering situation it will seldom be the case that the results of Chapters 2 through 4 can be applied without modification to the synthesis of a controller. An engineer may possess some *a priori* information on the relative probabilities of various elements of Θ, but usually it will not be sufficiently complete to permit him to assign a specific $\theta_0^* \in \Theta^*$ as the *a priori* probability distribution for θ. In Chapter 5 an example is considered which typifies some of the difficulties involved in formulating the desired properties of an optimal adaptive control rule. The process described here is of the class in which the plant transition properties are functionally dependent on a Markov process with an unknown statistical parameter. The analysis of this example illustrates how the engineer often must modify the framework introduced in Chapters 2 and 3 in order to design a compensation element in the presence of uncertainty about the characteristics of the plant. Since the max-cost ordering made Γ^* an equivalence class if the initial condition was placed on x_0, attention was restricted to a subclass of problems for which the performance criterion had meaning; i.e., $q \geqslant 2$ in Eq. (5.1).

In Chapter 6 a system was studied which was not amenable to direct application of the recurrence formula for the Bayes control policy. The succession of alternate minimizations and integrations can be performed readily only if ρ_j can be expressed as a simple function of the state and control variables. Much work in optimal control theory has been concentrated on systems for which ρ_j is a quadratic form for all $j \in [0, N]$. The requirement of learning which is implicit in the adaptive control policy makes it likely that the expected cost of the Bayes policy cannot be expressed in terms of known special functions. In such a case the intractable character of the problem forces the designer to search for a control policy which is a compromise between the exigencies of low performance index and ease of mechanization. The system examined in Chapter 6 illustrates some of these complexities.

It is interesting to observe parenthetically that although a control rule which is both extended Bayes and an equalizer is minimax, the equalizer characteristic cannot be viewed as an optimality property in itself. Thus, even though the closed-loop system may be completely insensitive to parameter variations, there may exist control policies with a uniformly smaller cost. For example, consider the system described by the equations

$$x_1 = ax_0 + \theta v_0$$

and

$$x_0 = x(0),$$

where

$$h(x, \bar{v}, \tilde{x}) = (x_1)^2$$

and

$$\Theta = \{\theta \mid 0 < \theta_1 \leqslant \theta \leqslant \theta_2 < \infty\}.$$

If v_0 can depend explicitly on x_0, then the control policy

$$\bar{u} = -\frac{ax_0}{\theta_2}$$

has a Bayes cost

$$H(\bar{u}, \theta) = (ax_0)^2 \left(1 - \frac{\theta}{\theta_2}\right)^2.$$

On the other hand, the equalizer $\bar{\omega} \equiv 0$ has a Bayes cost

$$H(\bar{\omega}, \theta) = (ax_0)^2.$$

Thus, it is apparent that $\bar{u}$ is better than $\bar{\omega}$. In fact any control rule of the form $\bar{v} = -ax_0/\tilde{\theta}$ where $\theta_2/2 < \tilde{\theta} \leqslant \theta_2$ is better than the equalizer.

This book has explored the relationship between a certain class of adaptive control system and fixed sample-size statistical games. The development has been restricted to problems in which the system is described by a set of difference equations and the optimization interval is fixed and finite. The question now arises as to the applicability of this work to continuous systems and systems with an infinite optimization period. The restriction that the mathematical model of the system be composed of a set of difference equations does not seem unnatural in most physical systems. If the loop contains inertial elements and if the control energy is bounded, a discrete time model of the process will be satisfactory if the time increment is chosen appropriately. In the same way, if the control policy approaches some constant form as N increases, this limiting control rule might be employed as a control policy for an infinite optimization interval.

Appendix A

From Eqs. (4.15) and (4.25),

$$\alpha_N = \int \frac{x_N{}^2 \prod_{i=0}^{N} \delta(x_i - \xi_{i-1}x_{i-1} - v_{i-1})[\prod_{i=0}^{N-1} p(\xi_i \mid \theta, \xi^{i-1})]^2}{\int \prod_{i=0}^{N-1} p(\xi_i \mid \eta, \xi^{i-1}) p_0(\eta)\, d\Omega(\eta)} p_0(\theta)\, d\Omega(\theta). \tag{A.1}$$

The criterion functional is independent of v_N. Therefore,

$$\hat{u}_N = c \tag{A.2}$$

where c is an arbitrary scalar. Consequently

$$\rho_N = \alpha_N .$$

Since $W_j = 0, 0 \leqslant j \leqslant N - 1$, it follows that $\alpha_j = 0, 0 \leqslant j \leqslant N - 1$.

$$\int \rho_N\, d\Omega(x_N) = \int \frac{(\xi_{N-1}x_{N-1} + v_{N-1})^2 \prod_{i=0}^{N-1} \delta(x_i - \xi_{i-1}x_{i-1} - v_{i-1})}{\int \prod_{i=0}^{N-1} p(\xi_i \mid \eta, \xi^{i-1}) p_0(\eta)\, d\Omega(\eta)}$$

$$\times \left[\prod_{i=0}^{N-1} p(\xi_i \mid \theta, \xi^{i-1}\right]^2 p_0(\theta)\, d\Omega(\theta). \tag{A.3}$$

To simplify the expression involving θ, note that

$$\int \prod_{i=0}^{N-1} p(\xi_i \mid \eta, \xi^{i-1}) p_0(\eta)\, d\Omega(\eta)$$

$$= \left(\frac{1}{\pi}\right)^{N/2} \frac{1}{\sqrt{2\pi}\sigma} \int_{-\infty}^{\infty} \exp\left(-\sum_{i=0}^{N-1} (\xi_i - \eta)^2\right) \exp\left(-\frac{(\eta - u)^2}{2\sigma^2}\right) d\eta$$

$$= \frac{(1/\pi)^{(N+1)/2}}{\sqrt{2}\sigma \sqrt{s + 1/2\sigma^2}} \exp\left\{-\sum_{i=0}^{N-1} \xi_i{}^2 - \frac{u}{2\sigma^2} + \frac{(\sum_{i=0}^{N-1} \xi_i - u/2\sigma^2)^2}{N + 1/2\sigma^2}\right\}.$$

Similarly,

$$\int \left[\prod_{i=0}^{N-1} p(\xi_i \mid \theta, \xi^{i-1}) \right]^2 p_0(\theta)\, d\theta$$

$$= \int_{-\infty}^{\infty} \left[\left(\frac{1}{\pi}\right)^{N/2} \exp\left(-\sum_{i=0}^{N-1} (\xi_i - \theta)^2\right) \right]^2 \frac{1}{\sqrt{2\pi}\sigma} \exp\left(-\frac{(\theta - u)^2}{2\sigma^2}\right) d\theta$$

$$= \frac{(1/\pi)^{(2N+1)/2}}{\sqrt{2}\sigma \sqrt{2s + 1/2\sigma^2}} \exp\left\{-2\sum_{i=0}^{N-1} \xi_i^2 - \frac{u}{2\sigma^2} + \frac{(2\sum_{i=0}^{N-1} \xi_i - u/2\sigma^2)^2}{2N + 1/2\sigma^2}\right\}.$$

Combining these equations,

$$\frac{\int [\prod_{i=0}^{N-1} p(\xi_i \mid \theta, \xi^{i-1})]^2 p_0(\theta)\, d\theta}{\int \prod_{i=0}^{N-1} p(\xi_i \mid \eta, \xi^{i-1}) p_0(\eta)\, d\eta} = \left(\frac{1}{\pi}\right)^{N/2} \sqrt{\frac{N + 1/2\sigma^2}{2N + 1/2\sigma^2}}$$

$$\times \exp\left\{-\sum_{i=0}^{N-1} \xi_i^2 + \frac{(2\sum_{i=0}^{N-1} \xi_i - u/2\sigma^2)^2}{2N + 1/2\sigma^2} - \frac{(\sum_{i=0}^{N-1} \xi_i - u/2\sigma^2)^2}{N + 1/2\sigma^2}\right\}. \quad \text{(A.4)}$$

Since $\bar{v}_{N-1}$ cannot be an explicit function of ξ_{N-1}, combine Eq. (A.4) with Eq. (A.3) and integrate out ξ_{N-1}:

$$\int \rho_N \, d\Omega(x_N, \xi_{N-1})$$

$$= N_1 \prod_{i=0}^{N-1} \delta(x_i - \xi_{i-1} x_{i-1} - v_{i-1})$$

$$\times \exp\left\{-\sum_{i=0}^{N-2} \xi_i^2 + \frac{(2\sum_{i=0}^{N-2} \xi_i - u/2\sigma^2)^2}{2N + 1/2\sigma^2} - \frac{(\sum_{i=0}^{N-2} \xi_i - u/2\sigma^2)^2}{N + 1/2\sigma^2}\right\}$$

$$\times \left(\int_{-\infty}^{\infty} (\xi_{N-1} x_{N-1} + v_{N-1})^2 \right.$$

$$\times \exp\left\{-\xi_{N-1}^2 + \frac{4\xi_{N-1}^2 + 4\xi_{N-1}(2\sum_{i=0}^{N-2} \xi_i - u/2\sigma^2)}{2N + 1/2\sigma^2}\right.$$

$$\left. \left. - \frac{\xi_{N-1}^2 + 2\xi_{N-1}(\sum_{i=0}^{N-2} \xi_i - u/2\sigma^2)}{N + 1/2\sigma^2}\right\} d\xi_{N-1}\right),$$

where

$$N_1 = \left(\frac{1}{\pi}\right)^{N/2} \sqrt{\frac{N + 1/2\sigma^2}{2N + 1/2\sigma^2}}.$$

The above expression can be written in the form

$$\int \rho_N \, d\Omega(x_N, \xi_{N-1})$$

$$= N_1 \prod_{i=0}^{N-1} \delta(x_i - \xi_{i-1}x_{i-1} - v_{i-1})$$

$$\times \exp\left\{ -\sum_{i=0}^{N-2} \xi_i^2 + \frac{(2\sum_{i=0}^{N-2} \xi_i - u/2\sigma^2)^2}{2N + 1/2\sigma^2} - \frac{(\sum_{i=0}^{N-2} \xi_i - u/2\sigma^2)^2}{N + 1/2\sigma^2} \right.$$

$$\left. + \frac{\left[-\dfrac{\sum_{i=0}^{N-2} \xi_i - u/2\sigma^2}{N + 1/2\sigma^2} + \dfrac{2(2\sum_{i=0}^{N-2} \xi_i - u/2\sigma^2)}{2N + 1/2\sigma^2} \right]^2}{1 + \dfrac{1}{N + 1/2\sigma^2} - \dfrac{4}{2N + 1/2\sigma^2}} \right\}$$

$$\times \int_{-\infty}^{\infty} (\xi_{N-1}x_{N-1} + v_{N-1})^2 \exp\left\{ -\left(1 + \frac{1}{N + 1/2\sigma^2} - \frac{4}{2N + 1/2\sigma^2}\right) \right. \tag{A.5}$$

$$\left. \times \left(\xi_{N-1} - \frac{-\dfrac{\sum_{i=0}^{N-2} \xi_i - u/2\sigma^2}{N + 1/2\sigma^2} + \dfrac{2(2\sum_{i=0}^{N-2} \xi_i - u/2\sigma^2)}{2N + 1/2\sigma^2}}{1 + \dfrac{1}{N + 1/2\sigma^2} - \dfrac{4}{2N + 1/2\sigma^2}} \right)^2 \right\} d\xi_{N-1}.$$

This is a rather long expression but it can be simplified by defining

$$a_{1,N-1} = 1 + \frac{1}{N + 1/2\sigma^2} - \frac{4}{2N + 1/2\sigma^2},$$

$$\tilde{a}_{2,N-1} = a_{2,N-1} = \frac{1}{N + 1/2\sigma^2},$$

$$\tilde{a}_{3,N-1} = a_{3,N-1} = \frac{1}{2N + 1/2\sigma^2},$$

$$a_{4,N-1} = 0.$$

Then, suppressing the obvious summation indices,

$$\int \rho_N \, d\Omega(x_N, \xi_{N-1})$$

$$= N_1 \prod^{N-1} \delta(x_i - \xi_{i-1}x_{i-1} - v_{i-1})$$

$$\times \exp\left\{-\sum^{N-2} \xi_i^2 + \tilde{a}_{3,N-1}\left(2\sum^{N-2} \xi_i - \frac{u}{2\sigma^2}\right)^2\right.$$

$$- \tilde{a}_{2,N-1}\left(\sum^{N-2} \xi_i - \frac{u}{2\sigma^2}\right)^2$$

$$+ \frac{[2a_{3,N-1}(2\sum^{N-2} \xi_i - u/2\sigma^2) - a_{2,N-1}(\sum^{N-2} \xi_i - u/2\sigma^2)]^2}{a_{1,N-1}}$$

$$\left. + a_{4,N-1}(2\sum^{N-2} \xi_i - u/2\sigma^2)(\sum^{N-2} \xi_i - u/2\sigma^2)\right\} \tag{A.6}$$

$$\times \int_{-\infty}^{\infty} (\xi_{N-1}x_{N-1} + v_{N-1})^2 \exp\left\{-a_{1,N-1}\left(\xi_{N-1}\right.\right.$$

$$\left.\left. - \frac{2a_{3,N-1}(2\sum^{N-2} \xi_i - u/2\sigma^2) - a_{2,N-1}(\sum^{N-2} \xi_i - u/2\sigma^2)}{a_{1,N-1}}\right)^2\right\} d\xi_{N-1} .$$

The following identity can easily be verified:

$$\int_{-\infty}^{\infty} (ax + b)^2 \exp[-c(x - d)^2] \, dx = \sqrt{\frac{\pi}{c}}\left[\frac{a^2}{2c} + (ad + b)^2\right].$$

Equation (A.6) becomes

$$\int \rho_N \, d\Omega(x_N, \xi_{N-1})$$

$$= N_1 \prod^{N-1} \delta(x_i - \xi_{i-1}x_{i-1} - v_{i-1})$$

$$\times \exp\left\{-\sum^{N-2} \xi_i^2 + \tilde{a}_{3,N-1}\left(2\sum^{N-2} \xi_i - \frac{u}{2\sigma^2}\right)^2\right.$$

$$- \tilde{a}_{2,N-1}\left(\sum^{N-2} \xi_i - \frac{u}{2\sigma^2}\right)^2$$

$$+\frac{[2a_{3,N-1}(2\sum^{N-2}\xi_i - u/2\sigma^2) - a_{2,N-1}(\sum^{N-2}\xi_i - u/2\sigma^2)]^2}{a_{1,N-1}}$$

$$+ a_{4,N-1}\left(2\sum^{N-2}\xi_i - \frac{u}{2\sigma^2}\right)\left(\sum^{N-2}\xi_i - \frac{u}{2\sigma^2}\right)\Bigg\}\Bigg(\frac{x_{N-1}^2}{2a_{1,N-1}}$$

$$+\left[\frac{x_{N-1}[2a_{3,N-1}(2\sum^{N-2}\xi_i - u/2\sigma^2) - a_{2,N-1}(\sum^{N-2}\xi_i - u/2\sigma^2)]}{a_{1,N-1}} + v_{N-1}\right]^2\Bigg).$$

The optimal v_{N-1} is given by

$$\hat{u}_{N-1} = -\frac{2a_{3,N-1}(2\sum^{N-2}\xi_i - u/2\sigma^2) - a_{2,N-1}(\sum^{N-2}\xi_i - u/2\sigma^2)}{a_{1,N-1}}x_{N-1}, \tag{A.7}$$

and

$$\rho_{N-1} = N_2 x_{N-1}^2 \prod^{N-1} \delta(x_i - \xi_{i-1}x_{i-1} - v_{i-1})$$

$$\times \exp\Bigg\{-\sum^{N-2}\xi_i^2 + \tilde{a}_{3,N-1}\left(2\sum^{N-2}\xi_i - \frac{u}{2\sigma^2}\right)^2$$

$$-\tilde{a}_{2,N-1}\left(\sum^{N-2}\xi_i - \frac{u}{2\sigma^2}\right)^2$$

$$+\frac{[2a_{3,N-1}(2\sum^{N-2}\xi_i - u/2\sigma^2) - a_{2,N-1}(\sum^{N-2}\xi_i - u/2\sigma^2)]^2}{a_{1,N-1}}$$

$$+ a_{4,N-1}\left(2\sum^{N-2}\xi_i - \frac{u}{2\sigma^2}\right)\left(\sum^{N-2}\xi_i - \frac{u}{2\sigma^2}\right)\Bigg\}$$

where

$$N_2 = \frac{\sqrt{\pi}N_1}{2(a_{1,N-1})^{3/2}}.$$

Hence, using the notation $\delta_i = \delta(x_i - \xi_{i-1}x_{i-1} - v_{i-1})$, we have

$$\int \rho_{N-1}\, d\Omega(x_{N-1}),$$

$$= N_2(\xi_{N-2}x_{N-2} + v_{N-2})^2 \prod^{N-2}\delta_i$$

$$\times \exp\left\{-\sum^{N-2}\xi_i + \tilde{a}_{3,N-1}\left(2\sum^{N-2}\xi_i - \frac{u}{2\sigma^2}\right)^2\right.$$

$$- \tilde{a}_{2,N-1}\left(\sum^{N-2}\xi_i - \frac{u}{2\sigma^2}\right)^2$$

$$+ \frac{[2a_{3,N-1}(2\sum^{N-2}\xi_i - u/2\sigma^2) - a_{2,N-1}(\sum^{N-2}\xi_i - u/2\sigma^2)]^2}{a_{1,N-1}}$$

$$\left. + a_{4,N-1}\left(2\sum^{N-2}\xi_i - \frac{u}{2\sigma^2}\right)\left(\sum^{N-2}\xi_i - \frac{u}{2\sigma^2}\right)\right\}. \qquad \text{(A.8)}$$

Since $\hat{\mu}_{N-2}$ cannot be an explicit function of ξ_{N-2}, this variable must be integrated out. Consider only the term in the exponential.

$$\{\ \} = -\sum^{N-3}\xi_i^{\,2} - \xi_{N-2}^2 + \tilde{a}_{3,N-1}\left(4\xi_{N-2}^2\right.$$

$$\left. + 4\xi_{N-2}\left(2\sum^{N-3}\xi_i - \frac{u}{2\sigma^2}\right) + \left(2\sum^{N-3}\xi_i - \frac{u}{2\sigma^2}\right)^2\right)$$

$$- \tilde{a}_{2,N-1}\left(\xi_{N-2}^2 + 2\xi_{N-2}\left(\sum^{N-3}\xi i - \frac{u}{2\sigma^2}\right)\right.$$

$$\left. + \left(\sum^{N-3}\xi_i - \frac{u}{2\sigma^2}\right)^2\right) + \frac{4a_{3,N-1}^2}{a_{1,N-1}}\left(4\xi_{N-2}^2 + 4\xi_{N-2}\right.$$

$$\left. \times \left(2\sum^{N-3}\xi_i - \frac{u}{2\sigma^2}\right) + \left(2\sum^{N-3}\xi_i - \frac{u}{2\sigma^2}\right)^2\right)$$

$$+ \frac{a_{2,N-1}^2}{a_{1,N-1}}\left(\xi_{N-2}^2 + 2\xi_{N-2}\left(\sum^{N-3}\xi_i - \frac{u}{2\sigma^2}\right)\right.$$

$$\left. + \left(\sum^{N-3}\xi_i - \frac{u}{2\sigma^2}\right)^2\right) + \left(a_{4,N-1} - \frac{4a_{3,N-1}a_{2,N-1}}{a_{1,N-1}}\right)$$

$$\times \left(2\xi_{N-2}^2 + \xi_{N-2}\left(2\sum^{N-3}\xi_i - \frac{u}{2\sigma^2}\right)\right.$$

$$\left. + 2\xi_{N-2}\left(\sum^{N-3}\xi_i - \frac{u}{2\sigma^2}\right) + \left(2\sum^{N-3}\xi_i - \frac{u}{2\sigma^2}\right)\left(\sum^{N-3}\xi_i - \frac{u}{2\sigma^2}\right)\right)$$

$$= -\sum^{N-3} \xi_i{}^2 + \left(\tilde{a}_{3,N-1} + \frac{4a^2_{3,N-1}}{a_{1,N-1}}\right)\left(2\sum^{N-2}\xi_i - \frac{u}{2\sigma^2}\right)^2$$

$$- \left(\tilde{a}_{2,N-1} - \frac{a^2_{2,N-1}}{a_{1,N-1}}\right)\left(\sum^{N-3}\xi_i - \frac{u}{2\sigma^2}\right)^2$$

$$+ \left(a_{4,N-1} - \frac{4a_{3,N-1}a_{2,N-1}}{a_{1,N-1}}\right)\left(2\sum^{N-3}\xi_i - \frac{u}{2\sigma^2}\right)$$

$$\times \left(\sum^{N-3}\xi_i - \frac{u}{2\sigma^2}\right) - \left(1 - 4\tilde{a}_{3,N-1} + \tilde{a}_{2,N-1} - \frac{16a^2_{3,N-1}}{a_{1,N-1}}\right.$$

$$\left. - \frac{a^2_{2,N-1}}{a_{1,N-1}} - 2a_{4,N-1} + \frac{8a_{3,N-1}a_{2,N-1}}{a_{1,N-1}}\right)$$

$$\times \xi^2_{N-2} + \left(4\tilde{a}_{3,N-1} + \frac{16a^2_{3,N-1}}{a_{1,N-1}} + a_{4,N-1} - \frac{4a_{3,N-1}a_{2,N-1}}{a_{1,N-1}}\right)$$

$$\times \xi_{N-2}\left(2\sum^{N-3}\xi_i - \frac{u}{2\sigma^2}\right) - \left(2\tilde{a}_{2,N-1} - \frac{2a^2_{2,N-1}}{a_{1,N-1}}\right.$$

$$\left. - 2a_{4,N-1} + 8\,\frac{a_{3,N-1}a_{2,N-1}}{a_{1,N-1}}\right)\xi_{N-2}\left(\sum^{N-3}\xi_i - \frac{u}{2\sigma^2}\right)^2. \tag{A.9}$$

Define

$$a_{1,N-2} = 1 - 4\tilde{a}_{3,N-1} + \tilde{a}_{2,N-1} - \frac{16a^2_{3,N-1}}{a_{1,N-1}} - \frac{a^2_{2,N-1}}{a_{1,N-1}} - 2a_{4,N-1} + \frac{8a_{3,N-1}a_{2,N-1}}{a_{1,N-1}},$$

$$a_{2,N-2} = \tilde{a}_{2,N-1} - \frac{a^2_{2,N-1}}{a_{1,N-1}} - a_{4,N-1} + \frac{4a_{3,N-1}a_{2,N-1}}{a_{1,N-1}},$$

$$a_{3,N-2} = \tilde{a}_{3,N-1} + \frac{4a^2_{3,N-1}}{a_{1,N-1}} + \frac{a_{4,N-1}}{4} - \frac{a_{3,N-1}a_{2,N-1}}{a_{1,N-1}}, \tag{A.10}$$

$$\tilde{a}_{2,N-2} = \tilde{a}_{2,N-1} - \frac{a^2_{2,N-1}}{a_{1,N-1}},$$

$$\tilde{a}_{3,N-2} = \tilde{a}_{3,N-1} + \frac{4a^2_{3,N-1}}{a_{1,N-1}},$$

$$a_{4,N-1} = a_{4,N-1} - \frac{4a_{3,N-1}a_{2,N-1}}{a_{1,N-1}}.$$

With these substitutions, Eq. (A.9) becomes

$$\begin{aligned}
\Big\{ \quad \Big\} = &- \sum^{N-3} \xi_i^2 + \tilde{a}_{3,N-2}\left(2\sum^{N-3} \xi_i - \frac{u}{2\sigma^2}\right)^2 \\
&- \tilde{a}_{2,N-2}\left(\sum^{N-2} \xi_i - \frac{u}{2\sigma^2}\right)^2 \\
&+ a_{4,N-2}\left(2\sum^{N-3} \xi_i - \frac{u}{2\sigma^2}\right)\left(\sum^{N-3} \xi_i - \frac{u}{2\sigma^2}\right) \\
&+ \frac{[2a_{3,N-2}(2\sum^{N-3} \xi_i - u/2\sigma^2) - a_{2,N-2}(\sum^{N-3} \xi_i - u/2\sigma^2)]^2}{a_{1,N-2}} \\
&- a_{1,N-2}\Bigg(\xi_{N-2} - \frac{2a_{3,N-2}(2\sum^{N-2} \xi_i - u/2\sigma^2)}{a_{1,N-2}} \\
&- \frac{a_{2,N-2}(\sum^{N-2} \xi_i - u/2\sigma^2)}{a_{1,N-2}}\Bigg)^2.
\end{aligned}$$

Substituting this expression into Eq. (A.8) yields a form exactly like Eq. (A.6). Therefore, $\hat{u}_{N-2}$ can be written by inspection,

$$\hat{u}_{N-2} = -\frac{2a_{3,N-2}(2\sum^{N-3} \xi_i - u/2\sigma^2) - a_{2,N-2}(\sum^{N-3} \xi_i - u/2\sigma^2)}{a_{1,N-2}} x_{N-2},$$

and

$$\begin{aligned}
\rho_{N-2} = N_3 x^2_{N-2} \prod_{i=0}^{N-2} \delta_i \exp \Bigg\{ &- \sum^{N-3} \xi_i^2 + \tilde{a}_{3,N-2}\left(2\sum^{N-3} \xi_i - \frac{u}{2\sigma^2}\right)^2 \\
&- \tilde{a}_{2,N-2}\left(\sum^{N-3} \xi_i - \frac{u}{2\sigma^2}\right)^2 \\
&+ a_{4,N-2}\left(2\sum^{N-3} \xi_i - \frac{u}{2\sigma^2}\right)\left(\sum^{N-3} \xi_i - \frac{u}{2\sigma^2}\right) \\
&+ \frac{[2a_{3,N-2}(2\sum^{N-3} \xi_i - u/2\sigma^2) - a_{2,N-2}(\sum^{N-3} \xi_i - u/2\sigma^2)]^2}{a_{1,N-2}} \Bigg\}.
\end{aligned} \tag{A.11}$$

The $a_{i,j}$ in Eq. (A.11) satisfy the following recurrence formula:

$$a_{1,N-1} = 1 + \frac{1}{N + 1/2\sigma^2} - \frac{4}{2N + 1/2\sigma^2},$$

$$\tilde{a}_{2,N-1} = a_{2,N-1} = \frac{1}{N + 1/2\sigma^2},$$

$$\tilde{a}_{3,N-1} = a_{3,N-1} = \frac{1}{2N + 1/2\sigma^2},$$

$$a_{4,N-1} = 0,$$

$$a_{1,j-1} = 1 - 4\tilde{a}_{3,j} + \tilde{a}_{2,j} + \frac{8a_{3,j}a_{2,j} - 16a_{3,j}^2 - a_{2,j}^2}{a_{1,j}} - 2a_{4,j},$$

$$a_{2,j-1} = \tilde{a}_{2,j} - a_{4,j} + \frac{4a_{3,j}a_{2,j} - a_{2,j}^2}{a_{1,j}}, \tag{A.12}$$

$$a_{3,j-1} = \tilde{a}_{3,j} + \frac{a_{4,j}}{4} + \frac{4a_{3,j}^2 - a_{3,j}a_{2,j}}{a_{1,j}},$$

$$\tilde{a}_{2,j-1} = \tilde{a}_{2,j} - \frac{a_{2,j}^2}{a_{1,j}},$$

$$\tilde{a}_{3,j-1} = \tilde{a}_{3,j} + \frac{4a_{3,j}^2}{a_{1,j}},$$

$$a_{4,j-1} = a_{4,j} - \frac{4a_{3,j}a_{2,j}}{a_{1,j}}.$$

Define the variable λ_j as follows:

$$\lambda_j = -\sum_{i=0}^{j-1} \xi_i^2 + \tilde{a}_{3,j}\left(2\sum^{j-1} \xi_i - \frac{\mu}{2\sigma^2}\right)^2 - \tilde{a}_{2,j}\left(\sum^{j-1} \xi_i - \frac{\mu}{2\sigma^2}\right)^2$$
$$\frac{[2a_{3,j}(2\sum^{j-1} \xi_i - \mu/2\sigma^2) - a_{2,j}(\sum^{j-1} \xi_i - \mu/2\sigma^2)]^2}{a_{1,j}} \tag{A.13}$$
$$+ a_{4,j}\left(2\sum^{j-1} \xi_i - \frac{\mu}{2\sigma^2}\right)\left(\sum^{j-1} \xi_i - \frac{\mu}{2\sigma^2}\right).$$

Now assume ρ_j takes the form

$$\rho_j = N_j x_j^2 \prod_{i=0}^{j} \delta_i \exp\{\lambda_j\}. \tag{A.14}$$

Performing the indicated integrations, we find that

$$\int \rho_j \, d\Omega(x_j, \xi_{j-1})$$

$$= K_j \prod_{i=0}^{j-1} \delta_i \left\{ \frac{x_{j-1}^2}{2a_{1,j-1}} + \left[v_{j-1} \right.\right.$$

$$\left.\left. + x_{j-1} \left(\frac{2a_{3,j-1}(2\sum^{j-2} \xi_i - \mu/2\sigma^2) - a_{2,j-1}(\sum^{j-2} \xi_i - \mu/2\sigma^2)}{a_{1,j-1}} \right) \right]^2 \right\}$$

$$\times \exp\{\lambda_{j-1}\}. \tag{A.15}$$

We can see directly from Eq. (A.15) that a Bayes control policy is given by

$$\hat{u}_j = -\frac{2a_{3,j}(2\sum^{j-1} \xi_i - \mu/2\sigma^2) - a_{2,j}(\sum^{j-1} \xi_i - \mu/2\sigma^2)}{a_{1,j}} x_j \tag{A.16}$$

and that

$$\rho_{j-1} = N_{j-1} x_{j-1}^2 \prod_{i=1}^{j-1} \delta_i \exp\{\lambda_{j-1}\}. \tag{A.17}$$

By induction it follows that a Bayes control policy is given by Eq. (A.16) for all integers j in the interval $1 \leqslant j \leqslant N$. Note that many Bayes policies are possible because v_N can be chosen arbitrarily.

Let us next consider the Bayes cost of the control process. From Eq. (A.17)

$$\rho_1 = N_1 x_1^2 \delta_1 \epsilon^{\lambda_1}.$$

It is interesting to note what happens to this index of performance as $\sigma^2 \to \infty$. From Eq. (A.17)

$$\lim_{\sigma^2 \to \infty} \lambda_1 = \xi_0^2 \left(-1 + \lim_{\sigma^2 \to \infty} \left\{ 4\tilde{a}_{3,1} - \tilde{a}_{2,1} + 2a_{4,1} + \frac{16a_{3,1}^2 + a_{2,1}^2 - 8a_{2,1}a_{3,1}}{a_{1,1}} \right\} \right).$$

It is shown in Appendix B that

$$\lim_{\sigma^2 \to \infty} a_{1,j} = \frac{j}{j+1},$$

$$\lim_{\sigma^2 \to \infty} a_{2,j} = \frac{1}{j+1},$$

$$\lim_{\sigma^2 \to \infty} a_{3,j} = \frac{1}{2(j+1)}.$$

Another identity which is contained in Eq. (A.12) is

$$4\tilde{a}_{3,j} - \tilde{a}_{2,j} + 2a_{4,j} = 4a_{3,j} - a_{2,j} .$$

Combining these relations we have

$$\lim_{\sigma^2 \to \infty} \lambda_1 = 0,$$

and

$$\lim_{\sigma^2 \to \infty} \rho_1 = N_1 x_1{}^2 \delta(x_1 - x(1)). \tag{A.18}$$

Appendix B

Proposition.

$$\lim_{\sigma\to\infty} a_{1,N-j} = \frac{N-j}{N-j+1},$$

$$\lim_{\sigma\to\infty} a_{2,N-j} = \frac{1}{N-j+1},$$

$$\lim_{\sigma\to\infty} a_{3,N-j} = \frac{1}{2(N-j+1)}.$$

Proof. Let $j = 1$. From Eq. (A.12) it is clear that

$$\lim_{\sigma\to\infty} a_{1,N-1} = 1 - \frac{1}{N} = \frac{N-1}{N},$$

$$\lim_{\sigma\to\infty} a_{2,N-1} = \frac{1}{N},$$

$$\lim_{\sigma\to\infty} a_{3,N-1} = \frac{1}{2N}.$$

Assume the assertion is true for $j = k + 1$, $k \geqslant 0$. Then

$$\begin{aligned}\lim_{\sigma\to\infty} a_{1,N-k-2} &= 1 - \frac{2}{N-k} + \frac{1}{N-k} - \frac{4}{(N-k)^2}\frac{N-k}{N-k-1} \\ &\quad + \frac{4}{(N-k)^2}\frac{N-k}{N-k-1} - \frac{1}{(N-k)^2}\frac{N-k}{N-k+1} \\ &= \frac{1}{N-k}\frac{(N-k+1)^2-1}{N-k-1} = \frac{N-k-2}{N-k+1},\end{aligned}$$

$$\begin{aligned}\lim_{\sigma\to\infty} a_{2,N-k-2} &= \frac{1}{N-k} - \frac{1}{(N-k)^2}\frac{N-k}{N-k-1} \\ &\quad + \frac{2}{(N-k)^2}\frac{N-k}{N-k-1} = \frac{1}{N-k-1},\end{aligned}$$

$$\lim_{\sigma\to\infty} a_{3,N-k-2} = \frac{1}{2(N-k)} + \frac{1}{(N-k)^2}\frac{N-k}{N-k-1} - \frac{1}{2(N-k)^2}\frac{N-k}{N-k-1} = \frac{1}{2(N-k-1)}.$$

The proposition is true for $j = 1$ and its truth for $j = k$ implies its truth for $j = k + 1$. Thus, the proposition is true for all $1 \leqslant j \leqslant N - 1$. ▼

Appendix C

In this appendix we will derive Eq. (5.7). It is interesting to study the form of this factor because it represents the manner in which the controller "learns" about the process. From Eq. (5.3) we see that

$$p(\xi_{i+1} \mid \xi_i, \theta) = \frac{1}{\sqrt{2\pi}\sigma} \exp \left\{ -\frac{1}{2\sigma^2} (\xi_{i+1} - \xi_i - \theta)^2 \right\}, \qquad i \geqslant 0.$$

Hence,

$$\prod_{i=1}^{j-1} p(\xi_i \mid \xi_{i-1}, \theta) = \left(\frac{1}{\sqrt{2\pi}\sigma} \right)^{j-1} \exp - \frac{1}{2\sigma^2} \sum_{i=1}^{j-1} (\xi_i - \xi_{i-1} - \theta)^2.$$

To simplify our notation, let us define:

$$a_{2,j} = \frac{1}{2\sigma^2} \sum_{i=1}^{j-1} (\xi_i - \xi_{i-1})^2,$$

$$a_{1,j} = \frac{1}{2\sigma^2} \sum_{i=1}^{j-1} (\xi_i - \xi_{i-1}).$$

Then

$$\prod_{i=1}^{j-1} p(\xi_i \mid \xi_{i-1}, \theta) = \left(\frac{1}{\sqrt{2\pi}\sigma} \right)^{j-1} \exp \left\{ -a_{2,j} + 2\theta a_{1,j} - \frac{(j-1)\theta^2}{2\sigma^2} \right\}.$$

Therefore,

$$\frac{1}{\sqrt{2\pi n}\sigma} \int_{-\infty}^{\infty} \prod_{i=1}^{j-1} p(\xi_i \mid \xi_{i-1}, \theta) \exp \left\{ -\frac{\theta^2}{2n\sigma^2} \right\} d\theta$$

$$= \left(\frac{1}{\sqrt{2\pi}\sigma} \right)^{j-1} \frac{1}{\sqrt{2\pi n}\sigma} \exp \left\{ -a_{2,j} + \frac{a_{1,j}^2}{[(j-1)/2\sigma^2] + 1/2n\sigma^2} \right\}$$

$$\times \int_{-\infty}^{\infty} \exp \left\{ -\left(\frac{j-1}{2\sigma^2} + \frac{1}{2n\sigma^2} \right) \left(\theta - \frac{a_{1,j}}{[(j-1)/2\sigma^2] + 1/2n\sigma^2} \right)^2 d\theta \right.$$

$$= \left(\frac{1}{\sqrt{2\pi}\sigma}\right)^{j-1} \frac{1}{\sqrt{2\pi n}\sigma} \frac{\sqrt{\pi}}{\sqrt{[(j-1)/2\sigma^2] + 1/2n\sigma^2}}$$

$$\times \exp\left\{-a_{2,j} + \frac{a_{1,j}^2}{[(j-1)/2\sigma^2] + 1/2n\sigma^2}\right\}.$$

In a similar manner one can show that

$$\frac{1}{\sqrt{2\pi n}\sigma} \int_{-\infty}^{\infty} \left[\prod_{i=1}^{j-1} p(\xi_i \mid \xi_{i-1}, \theta)\right]^2 \exp\left\{-\frac{\theta^2}{2n\sigma^2}\right\} d\theta$$

$$= \left(\frac{1}{\sqrt{2\pi}\sigma}\right)^{2j-2} \frac{1}{\sqrt{2\pi n}\sigma} \frac{\sqrt{\pi}}{\sqrt{[(j-1)/\sigma^2] + 1/2n\sigma^2}}$$

$$\times \exp\left\{-2a_{2,j} + \frac{4a_{1,j}^2}{[(j-1)/\sigma^2] + 1/2n\sigma^2}\right\}.$$

Thus,

$$\int \frac{[\prod_{i=1}^{j-1} p(\xi_i \mid \xi_{i-1}, \theta)]^2}{\int \prod_{i=1}^{j-1} p(\xi_i \mid \xi_{i-1}, \theta)\, d\theta^*_{n\sigma^2}}\, d\theta^*_{n\sigma^2}$$

$$= \left(\frac{1}{\sqrt{2\pi}\sigma}\right)^{j-1} \sqrt{\frac{[(j-1)/2\sigma^2] + 1/2n\sigma^2}{[(j-1)/\sigma^2] + 1/2n\sigma^2}}$$

$$\times \exp\left\{-a_{2,j} + \left(\frac{4}{[(j-1)/\sigma^2] + 1/2n\sigma^2} - \frac{1}{[(j-1)/2\sigma^2] + 1/2n\sigma^2}\right) a_{1,j}^2\right\}.$$

Since we wish to study the behavior of this factor for large n, the following asymptotic relations may be used:

$$\frac{4}{[(j-1)/\sigma^2] + 1/2n\sigma^2} - \frac{1}{[(j-1)/2\sigma^2] + 1/2n\sigma^2} = \frac{2\sigma^2}{j-1}\left(1 - \frac{1}{2n^2(j-1)^2}\right) + O\left(\frac{1}{n^3}\right),$$

$$\sqrt{\frac{[(j-1)/2\sigma^2] + 1/2n\sigma^2}{[(j-1)/\sigma^2] + 1/2n\sigma^2}} = \sqrt{\frac{1}{2}}\sqrt{1 + \frac{1}{2n(j-1)}} + O\left(\frac{1}{n}\right).$$

Thus,

$$\int \frac{[\prod_{i=1}^{j-1} p(\xi_i \mid \xi_{i-1}, \theta)]^2}{\int \prod_{i=1}^{j-1} p(\xi_i \mid \xi_{i-1}, \theta)\, d\theta^*_{n\sigma^2}}\, d\theta^*_{n\sigma^2}$$

$$= \frac{1}{\sqrt{2}} \left(\frac{1}{\sqrt{2\pi\sigma}}\right)^{j-1} \exp\left\{-a_{2,j} + \frac{2\sigma^2}{j-1}\, a_{1,j}^2\right\} + O\left(\frac{1}{\sqrt{n}}\right).$$

Appendix D

In this appendix we will show explicitly the steps necessary to go from Eq. (5.9) to Eq. (5.10). From Eq. (5.9),

$$\int \rho_N(\eta)\, d\Omega(x_N)$$

$$= \int [\tilde{x}_N - H(\phi_{N-1}x_{N-1} + \Delta_{N-1} + v_{N-1} + \Theta_{N-1}\eta_{N-1})]^2$$

$$\times \prod_{i=0}^{N-1} \delta x_i \left[\left(\frac{1}{\sqrt{2\pi}\sigma_w}\right)^N \exp\left\{-\frac{1}{2\sigma_w{}^2}\sum_{i=1}^{N}(\tilde{x}_i - \tilde{x}_{i-1})^2\right\}\right]$$

$$\times \prod_{i=0}^{N-1} p(\eta_i)\left[\left(\frac{1}{\sqrt{2\pi}\sigma}\right)^{N-1}\frac{1}{\sqrt{2}}\exp\left\{-a_{2,N-1} + \frac{2\sigma^2}{N-1}a_{1,N-1}^2\right\}\right.$$

$$\left. + O\left(\frac{1}{\sqrt{n}}\right)\right] d\Omega(\eta^{N-1}).$$

Integrating with respect to $\tilde{x}_N$, we have

$$\int \rho_N(n)\, d\Omega(\tilde{x}_N, x_N)$$

$$= \int [\sigma_w{}^2 + (\tilde{x}_{N-1} - H(\phi_{N-1}x_{N-1} + \Delta_{N-1}v_{N-1} + \Theta_{N-1}\eta_{N-1}))]^2$$

$$\times \prod_{i=0}^{N-1} \delta x_i \left[\left(\frac{1}{\sqrt{2\pi}\sigma_w}\right)^{N-1} \exp\left\{-\frac{1}{2\sigma_w{}^2}\sum_{i=1}^{N-1}(\tilde{x}_i - \tilde{x}_{i-1})^2\right\}\right]$$

$$\times \prod_{i=0}^{N-1} p(\eta_i)\left[\left(\frac{1}{\sqrt{2\pi}\sigma}\right)^{N-1}\frac{1}{\sqrt{2}}\exp\left\{-a_{2,N-1} + \frac{2\sigma^2}{N-1}a_{1,N-1}^2\right\}\right.$$

$$\left. + O\left(\frac{1}{\sqrt{n}}\right)\right] d\Omega(\eta^{N-1}).$$

Because $E(\eta_i) = 0$, all linear terms in η_{N-1} vanish. Therefore,

$$\int \rho_N(n)\, d\Omega(x_N, \tilde{x}_N)$$

$$= \int [\sigma_w{}^2 + (H\Theta_{N-1})^2\sigma_\lambda{}^2 + (\tilde{x}_{N-1} - H(\phi_{N-1}x_{N-1} + \Delta_{N-1}v_{N-1}))^2]$$

$$\times \prod_{i=0}^{N-1} \delta x_i \left[\left(\frac{1}{\sqrt{2\pi}\sigma_w}\right)^{N-1} \exp\left\{-\frac{1}{2\sigma_w{}^2}\sum_{i=1}^{N-1}(\tilde{x}_i - \tilde{x}_{i-1})^2\right\}\right]$$

$$\times \prod_{i=0}^{N-2} p(\eta_i)\left[\left(\frac{1}{\sqrt{2\pi}\sigma}\right)^{N-1}\frac{1}{\sqrt{2}}\exp\left\{-a_{2,N-1} + \frac{2\sigma^2}{N-1}a_{1,N-1}^2\right\}\right.$$

$$\left.+ O\left(\frac{1}{\sqrt{n}}\right)\right] d\Omega(\eta^{N-2}).$$

If $H_{N-1}(\xi_{N-1})$ is any integrable function of ξ_{N-1}, we define

$$\sqrt{\frac{N-2}{2\pi\sigma^2(N-1)}}\int_{-\infty}^{\infty} H_{N-1}(\xi_{N-1})$$

$$\times \exp\left\{-\frac{N-2}{2\sigma^2(N-1)}\left(\xi_{N-1} - \xi_{N-2} - \frac{2\sigma^2}{N-2}a_{1,N-2}\right)^2\right\} d\xi_{N-1} = \bar{H}_{N-1}.$$

Now let us use the identity given in Eq. (E.3).

$$\int \rho_N(n)\, d\Omega(\tilde{x}_N, x_N, \xi_{N-1})$$

$$= \sqrt{\frac{N-1}{N-2}}\int [\sigma_w{}^2 + \overline{(H\Theta)^2}\sigma_\lambda{}^2 + \overline{(\tilde{x}_{N-1} - H\phi_{N-1}x_{N-1})^2}$$

$$- 2v_{N-1}\,\overline{H\Delta_{N-1}(x_{N-1} - H\phi_{N-1}x_{N-1})} + (v_{N-1})^2\,\overline{(H\Delta_{N-1})^2}]$$

$$\times \prod_{i=0}^{N-1} \delta x_i \left[\left(\frac{1}{\sqrt{2\pi}\sigma_w}\right)^{N-1} \exp\left\{-\frac{1}{2\sigma_w{}^2}\sum_{i=1}^{N-1}(\tilde{x}_i - \tilde{x}_{i-1})^2\right\}\right]$$

$$\times \prod_{i=0}^{N-2} p(\eta_i)\left[\left(\frac{1}{\sqrt{2\pi}\sigma}\right)^{N-2}\frac{1}{\sqrt{2}}\exp\left\{-a_{2,N-2} + \frac{2\sigma^2}{N-2}a_{1,N-2}^2\right\}\right.$$

$$\left.+ O\left(\frac{1}{\sqrt{n}}\right)\right] d\Omega(\eta^{N-2}).$$

Combining the above equation with Eq. (5.8), we have

$$\int \rho_N(n)\, d\Omega(\tilde{x}_N, x_N, \xi_{N-1}) + \alpha_{N-1}(n)$$

$$= \sqrt{\frac{N-1}{N-2}} \int \Big[\sigma_w{}^2 + \overline{(H\Theta)^2}\sigma_\lambda{}^2 + \tilde{x}_{N-1}^2$$

$$- 2\tilde{x}_{N-1}\, \overline{H\phi_{N-1}}\, x_{N-1} + x_{N-1}^T\, \overline{\phi_{N-1}^T H^T H \phi_{N-1}}\, x_{N-1}$$

$$- 2v_{N-1}\, \overline{H\Delta_{N-1}(\tilde{x}_{N-1} - H\phi_{N-1}x_{N-1})} + (v_{N-1})^2\, \overline{(H\Delta_{N-1})^2}$$

$$+ \sqrt{\frac{N-2}{N-1}}((\tilde{x}_{N-1} - Hx_{N-1})^2 + \beta_{N-1}v_{N-1}^2)\Big] \tag{D.1}$$

$$\times \prod_{i=0}^{N-1} \delta x_i \left[\left(\frac{1}{\sqrt{2\pi}\sigma_w}\right)^{N-1} \exp\left\{-\frac{1}{2\sigma_w{}^2}\sum_{i=1}^{N-1}(\tilde{x}_i - \tilde{x}_{i-1})^2\right\}\right]$$

$$\times \prod_{i=0}^{N-1} p(\eta_i) \left[\left(\frac{1}{\sqrt{2\pi}\sigma}\right)^{N-2} \frac{1}{\sqrt{2}} \exp\left\{-a_{2,N-2} + \frac{2\sigma^2}{N-2} a_{1,N-2}^2\right\}\right.$$

$$\left. + O\left(\frac{1}{\sqrt{n}}\right)\right] d\Omega(\eta^{N-2}).$$

To minimize the above expression with respect to v_{N-1}, we need only investigate the first bracketed term since all of the rest of the expression is positive. Hence, the optimal v_{N-1} is given by

$$\overline{u(n)_{N-1}} = \frac{\overline{H\Delta_{N-1}(\tilde{x}_{N-1} - H\phi_{N-1}x_{N-1})}}{\overline{(H\Delta_{N-1})^2} + \sqrt{(N-2)/(N-1)}\,\beta_{N-1}} + O\left(\frac{1}{\sqrt{n}}\right). \tag{D.2}$$

Substituting Eq. (D.1) into Eq. (D.2), we find that

$$\rho_{N-1}(n) = \min_{v_{N-1}} \int \rho_N(n)\, d\Omega(\tilde{x}_N, x_N, \xi_{N-1}) + \alpha_{N-1}(n),$$

$$= \sqrt{\frac{N-1}{N-2}} \int \Big[\sigma_w{}^2 + \overline{(H\Theta)^2}\,\sigma_\lambda{}^2 + \tilde{x}_{N-1}^2 R_{N-1} + \tilde{x}_{N-1}Q_{N-1}x_{N-1}$$

$$+ x_{N-1}^T P_{N-1}x_{N-1} + \sqrt{\frac{N-2}{N-1}}(\tilde{x}_{N-1} - Hx_{N-1})^2\Big]$$

$$\times \prod_{i=0}^{N-1} \delta x_i \left[\left(\frac{1}{\sqrt{2\pi}\sigma_w} \right)^{N-1} \exp \left\{ - \frac{1}{2\sigma_w^2} \sum_{i=1}^{N-1} (\tilde{x}_i - \tilde{x}_{i-1})^2 \right\} \right]$$

$$\times \prod_{i=0}^{N-2} p(\eta_i) \left[\left(\frac{1}{\sqrt{2\pi}\sigma} \right)^{N-2} \frac{1}{\sqrt{2}} \exp \left\{ -a_{2,N-2} + \frac{\sigma^2}{N-2} a_{1,N-2}^2 \right\} \right.$$

$$\left. + O\left(\frac{1}{\sqrt{n}} \right) \right] d\Omega(\eta^{N-1}), \tag{D.3}$$

where

$$R_{N-1} = 1 + \frac{(\overline{H\Delta_{N-1}})^2}{M_{N-1}},$$

$$Q_{N-1} = -2\overline{H\phi_{N-1}} - \frac{2\overline{H\Delta_{N-1}}\,\overline{H\Delta_{N-1}H\phi_{N-1}}}{M_{N-1}},$$

$$P_{N-1} = \overline{\phi_{N-1}^T H^T H \phi_{N-1}} + \frac{\overline{(\phi_{N-1}^T H^T \Delta_{N-1}^T H^T)}\,\overline{(H\Delta_{N-1}H\phi_{N-1})}}{M_{N-1}},$$

$$M_{N-1} = \overline{(H\Delta_{N-1})^2} + \sqrt{\frac{N-2}{N-1}}\,\beta_{N-1}\,. \tag{D.4}$$

Note that $\int \rho_N(n)\, d\Omega(\tilde{x}_N, x_N, \xi_N) + \alpha_{N-1}(n)$ is continuous in v_{N-1} if all of the averages in Eq. D.3 are bounded. Hence, any bounded change in v_{N-1} will result in a bounded change in the Bayes cost.

Appendix E

In this appendix we will derive the recurrence formula for the $\rho(n)$ and find the optimal $\overline{u(n)}$. For simplicity we will not show explicitly terms of order $1/\sqrt{n}$. Let us assume that ρ_{N-j} has the following form:

$$\rho_{N-j} = \int \{L_{N-j}(\xi, \eta) + x_{N-j}^T P_{N-j} x_{N-j} + R_{N-j}\tilde{x}_{N-j}^2 + Q_{N-j} x_{N-j}\tilde{x}_{N-j}$$

$$+ A_{N-j}(\tilde{x}_{N-j} - Hx_{N-j})^2\}$$

$$\times K_{N-j} \prod_{i=0}^{N-j} \delta(x_i - \phi_{i-1}x_{i-1} - \Delta_{i-1}v_{i-1} - \Theta_{i-1}\eta_{i-1})$$

$$\times \prod_{i=0}^{N-j-1} p(\eta_i) \left[\left(\frac{1}{\sqrt{2\pi\sigma_w}}\right)^{N-j} \exp\left\{-\frac{1}{2\sigma_w{}^2}\sum_{i=1}^{N-j}(\tilde{x}_i - \tilde{x}_{i-1})^2\right\}\right]$$

$$\left[\left(\frac{1}{\sqrt{2\pi\sigma}}\right)^{N-j-1} \exp\left\{-a_{2,N-j-1} + \frac{2\sigma^2}{N-j-1}\, a_{1,N-j-1}^2\right\}\right] d\Omega(\eta^{N-j-1}).$$

Integrating with respect to x_{N-j}, we obtain

$$\int \rho_{N-j}\, d\Omega(x_{N-j})$$

$$= \int \{L_{N-j}(\xi, \eta) + \eta_{N-j-1}^T \Theta_{N-j-1}^T (P_{N-j} + A_{N-j}H^TH)\Theta_{N-j-1}\eta_{N-j-1}$$

$$+ x_{N-j-1}^T \phi_{N-j-1}^T (P_{N-j} + A_{N-j}H^TH)\phi_{N-j-1}x_{N-j-1}$$

$$+ v_{N-j-1}^2 \Delta_{N-j-1}^T (P_{N-j} + A_{N-j}H^TH)\Delta_{N-j-1}$$

$$+ 2v_{N-j-1}(x_{N-j-1}^T \phi_{N-j-1}^T P_{N-j}\Delta_{N-j-1}$$

$$- A_{N-j}H\Delta_{N-j-1}\tilde{x}_{N-j} + A_{N-j}H\phi_{N-j-1}x_{N-j-1}H\Delta_{N-j-1}$$

$$+ \tfrac{1}{2}Q_{N-j}\Delta_{N-j-1}\tilde{x}_{N-j}) + \tilde{x}_{N-j}^2(R_{N-j} + A_{N-j})$$

$$+ 2\eta_{N-j-1}(x_{N-j-1}^T\phi_{N-j-1}^T P_{N-j}\Theta_{N-j}$$

$$+ v_{N-j-1}\Delta_{N-j-1}^T P_{N-j}\Theta_{N-j-1} + \tfrac{1}{2}Q_{N-j}\Theta_{N-j-1}\tilde{x}_{N-j}$$

$$+ A_{N-j}(-H\Theta_{N-j-1}\tilde{x}_{N-j} + 2H\phi_{N-j-1}x_{N-j-1}H\Theta_{N-j-}$$

$$+ 2H\Delta_{N-j-1}v_{N-j-1}H\Theta_{n-j-1})) + \tilde{x}_{N-j}(Q_{N-j}\phi_{N-j-1}$$

$$- 2A_{N-j}H\phi_{N-j-1})x_{N-j-1}\}$$

$$\times K_{N-j}\prod_{i=0}^{N-j-1}\delta(x_i - \phi_{i-1}x_{i-1} - \Delta_{i-1}v_{i-1} - \Theta_{i-1}\eta_{i-1})$$

$$\times \prod_{i=0}^{N-j-1} p(\eta_i)\left[\left(\frac{1}{\sqrt{2\pi}\sigma_w}\right)^{N-j}\exp\left\{-\frac{1}{2\sigma_w{}^2}\sum_{i=1}^{N-j}(\tilde{x}_i - \tilde{x}_{i-1})^2\right\}\right]$$

$$\times\left[\left(\frac{1}{\sqrt{2\pi}\sigma}\right)^{N-j-1}\exp\left\{-a_{2,N-j-1} + \frac{2\sigma^2}{N-j-1}a_{1,N-j-1}^2\right\}\right]d\Omega(\eta^{N-j-1}).$$

Next we will integrate with respect to $\tilde{x}_{N-j}$ and η_{N-j-1}, and obtain

$$\int \rho_{N-j}\, d\Omega(x_{N-j}, \tilde{x}_{N-j})$$

$$= \int\{\hat{L}_{N-j}(\xi, \eta) + \sigma_\lambda{}^2\Theta_{N-j-1}^T(P_{N-j} + A_{N-j}H^TH)\Theta_{N-j-1}$$

$$+ x_{N-j-1}^T\phi_{N-j-1}^T(P_{N-j} + A_{N-j}H^TH)\phi_{N-j-1}x_{N-j-1}$$

$$+ v_{N-j-1}^2\Delta_{N-j-1}^T(P_{N-j} + A_{N-j}H^TH)\Delta_{N-j-1}$$

$$+ 2v_{N-j-1}(x_{N-j-1}^T\phi_{N-j-1}^T P_{N-j}\Delta_{N-j-1}$$

$$- A_{N-j}H\Delta_{N-j-1}\tilde{x}_{N-j-1} + A_{N-j}H\phi_{N-j-1}x_{N-j-1}H\Delta_{N-j-1}$$

$$+ \tfrac{1}{2}Q_{N-j}\Delta_{N-j-1}\tilde{x}_{N-j-1}) + (\sigma_w{}^2 + \tilde{x}_{N-j-1}^2)(R_{N-j} + A_{N-j})$$

$$+ \tilde{x}_{N-j-1}(Q_{N-j}\phi_{N-j-1} - 2A_{N-j}H\phi_{N-j-1})x_{N-j-1}\}$$

$$\times K_{N-j}\prod_{i=0}^{N-j-1}\delta(x_i - \phi_{i-1}x_{i-1} - \Delta_{i-1}v_{i-1} - \theta_{i-1}\eta_{i-1}) \tag{E.1}$$

$$\times \prod_{i=0}^{N-j-2} p(\eta_i) \left[\left(\frac{1}{\sqrt{2\pi}\sigma_w} \right)^{N-j-1} \exp \left\{ -\frac{1}{2\sigma_w^2} \sum_{i=1}^{N-j-1} (\tilde{x}_i - \tilde{x}_{i-1})^2 \right\} \right]$$

$$\times \left[\left(\frac{1}{\sqrt{2\pi}\sigma} \right)^{N-j-1} \exp \left\{ -a_{2,N-j-1} + \frac{2\sigma^2}{N-j-1} a_{1,N-j-1}^2 \right\} \right] d\Omega(\eta^{N-j-2}), \tag{E.1 cont.}$$

where

$$\hat{L}_{N-j}(\xi, \eta) = \int L_{N-j}(\xi, \eta) p(\eta_{N-j-1}) \, d\Omega(\eta_{N-j-1}).$$

Now we must eliminate ξ_{N-j-1}. For this purpose we note that

$$-a_{2,N-j-1} + \frac{2\sigma^2}{N-j-1} a_{1,N-j-1}^2$$

$$= \frac{1}{2\sigma^2} \sum_{i=1}^{N-j-1} (\xi_i - \xi_{i-1})^2 + \frac{2\sigma^2}{N-j-1} \left[\frac{1}{2\sigma^2} \sum_{i=1}^{N-j-1} (\xi_i - \xi_{i-1}) \right]^2$$

$$= -\frac{1}{2\sigma^2} \sum_{i=1}^{N-j-2} (\xi_i - \xi_{i-1})^2 + \frac{2\sigma^2}{N-j-1} \left[\frac{1}{2\sigma^2} \sum_{i=1}^{N-j-2} (\xi_i - \xi_{i-1}) \right]^2$$

$$- \frac{1}{2\sigma^2} (\xi_{N-j-1} - \xi_{N-j-2})^2 + \frac{2\sigma^2}{N-j-1} \left[\frac{1}{2\sigma^2} (\xi_{N-j-1} - \xi_{N-j-2}) \right]^2$$

$$+ \frac{2\sigma^2}{N-j-1} \left(\frac{2}{4\sigma^4} (\xi_{N-j-1} - \xi_{N-j-2}) \sum_{i=1}^{N-j-2} (\xi_i - \xi_{i-1}) \right)$$

$$= -a_{2,N-j-2} + \frac{2\sigma^2}{N-j-1} a_{1,N-j-2}^2$$

$$+ (\xi_{N-j-1} - \xi_{N-j-2})^2 \left[-\frac{1}{2\sigma^2} + \frac{1}{(N-j-1)2\sigma^2} \right]$$

$$+ \frac{2\sigma^2}{N-j-1} a_{1,N-j-2} \frac{2}{2\sigma^2} (\xi_{N-j-1} - \xi_{N-j-2})$$

$$= -a_{2,N-j-2} + \frac{2\sigma^2}{N-j-2} a_{1,N-j-2}^2$$

$$- \frac{N-j-2}{2\sigma^2(N-j-1)} \left(\xi_{N-j-1} - \xi_{N-j-2} - \frac{2\sigma^2}{N-j-2} a_{1,N-j-2} \right)^2.$$

Define

$$g_{N-j-1}(\xi) = \frac{N-j-2}{2\sigma^2(N-j-1)}\left(\xi_{N-j-1} - \xi_{N-j-2} - \frac{2\sigma^2}{N-j-2}\, a_{1,N-j-2}\right)^2. \tag{E.2}$$

Then the following relation obtains:

$$-a_{2,N-j-1} + \frac{2\sigma^2}{N-j-1}\, a_{1,N-j-1}^2 = -a_{2,N-j-2} + \frac{2\sigma^2}{N-j-2}\, a_{1,N-j-2}^2 + g_{N-j-1}(\xi). \tag{E.3}$$

Given any function $H(\xi_{N-j-1})$ for which the following integral exists define:

$$\sqrt{\frac{N-j-2}{2\pi\sigma^2(N-j-1)}}\int_{-\infty}^{\infty} H(\xi_{N-j-1}) \exp\{g_{N-j-1}(\xi)\}\, d\xi_{N-j-1} = \bar{H}. \tag{E.4}$$

Note that the normalization of the integral is such that if H is independent of ξ_{N-j-1}, then $\bar{H} = H$. We are now in a position to eliminate ξ_{N-j-1} from Eq. (E.1).

$$\begin{aligned}
&\int \rho_{N-j}\, d\Omega(x_{N-j}, \tilde{x}_{N-j}, \xi_{N-j-1}) \\
&\quad = \int \{L_{N-j-1}(\xi, \eta) + x_{N-j-1}^T\, \overline{\phi_{N-j-1}^T(P_{N-j} + A_{N-j}H^TH)\phi_{N-j-1}}\, x_{N-j-1} \\
&\qquad + v_{N-j-1}^2\, \overline{\Delta_{N-j-1}^T(P_{N-j} + A_{N-j}H^TH)\Delta_{N-j-1}} \\
&\qquad + 2v_{N-j-1}(x_{N-j-1}^T\, \overline{\phi_{N-j-1}^T P_{N-j}\Delta_{N-j-1}} - A_{N-j}\, \overline{H\Delta_{N-j-1}}\, \tilde{x}_{N-j-1} \\
&\qquad + A_{N-j}\, \overline{H\Delta_{N-j-1}H\phi_{N-j-1}}\, x_{N-j-1} + \tfrac{1}{2}\overline{Q_{N-j}\Delta_{N-j-1}}\, \tilde{x}_{N-j-1}) \\
&\qquad + \tilde{x}_{N-j-1}(\overline{R_{N-j}} + A_{N-j}) + \tilde{x}_{N-j-1}(\overline{Q_{N-j}\phi_{N-j-1}} - 2A_{N-j}\overline{H\phi_{N-j-1}})x_{N-j-1}\} \\
&\qquad \times \sqrt{\frac{N-j-1}{N-j-2}}\, K_{N-j} \prod_{i=0}^{N-j-1} \delta(x_i - \phi_{i-1}x_{i-1} - \Delta_{i-1}v_{i-1} - \theta_{i-1}\eta_{i-1}) \prod_{i=0}^{N-j-2} p(\eta_i) \\
&\qquad \times \left[\left(\frac{1}{\sqrt{2\pi}\sigma_w}\right)^{N-j-1} \exp\left\{-\frac{1}{2\sigma_w{}^2}\sum_{i=1}^{N-j-1}(\tilde{x}_i - \tilde{x}_{i-1})^2\right\}\right] \\
&\qquad \times \left[\left(\frac{1}{\sqrt{2\pi}\sigma}\right)^{N-j-2} \exp\left\{-a_{2,N-j-2} + \frac{2\sigma^2}{N-j-2}\, a_{1,N-j-2}^2\right\}\right] d\Omega(\eta^{N-j-2}),
\end{aligned}$$

where

$$L_{N-j-1}(\xi, \eta) = \overline{\hat{L}_{N-j}(\xi, \eta)} + \sigma_\lambda{}^2 \overline{\Theta^T_{N-j-1}(P_{N-j} + A_{N-j}H^TH)\Theta_{N-j-1}}$$
$$+ \sigma_w{}^2(\overline{R_{N-j}} + A_{N-j}).$$

From Eq. (5.8)

$$\alpha_{N-j-1} = \int \{(\tilde{x}_{N-j-1} - Hx_{N-j-1})^2 + \beta_{N-j-1}v^2_{N-j-1}\}$$
$$\times \frac{1}{\sqrt{2}} \prod_{i=0}^{N-j-1} \delta(x_i - \phi_{i-1}x_{i-1} - \Delta_{i-1}v_{i-1} - \Theta_{i-1}\eta_{i-1})$$
$$\times \prod_{i=0}^{N-j-2} p(\eta_i) \left[\left(\frac{1}{\sqrt{2\pi}\sigma_w}\right)^{N-j-1} \exp\left\{-\frac{1}{2\sigma_w{}^2} \sum_{i=1}^{N-j-1} (\tilde{x}_i - \tilde{x}_{i-1})^2\right\}\right]$$
$$\times \left[\left(\frac{1}{\sqrt{2\pi}\sigma}\right)^{N-j-2} \exp\left\{-a_{2,N-j-2} + \frac{2\sigma^2}{N-j-2}a_{1,N-j-2}\right\}\right] d\Omega(\eta^{N-j-2}).$$

Therefore,

$$\int \rho_{N-j}\, d\Omega(x_{N-j}, \tilde{x}_{N-j}, \xi_{N-j-1}) + \alpha_{N-j-1}$$
$$= \int \Big\{L_{N-j-1}(\xi, \eta) + x^T_{N-j-1} \overline{\phi^T_{N-j-1}(P_{N-j} + A_{N-j}H^TH)\phi_{N-j-1}}\, x_{N-j-1}$$
$$+ v^2_{N-j-1} (\overline{\Delta^T_{N-j-1}(P_{N-j} + A_{N-j}H^TH)\, \Delta_{N-j-1}})$$
$$+ 2v_{N-j-1}(x^T_{N-j-1} \overline{\phi^T_{N-j-1}P_{N-j}\Delta_{N-j-1}} - A_{N-j}\, \overline{H\Delta_{N-j-1}}\, \tilde{x}_{N-j-1} \tag{E.5}$$
$$+ A_{N-j}\, \overline{H\Delta_{N-j-1}H\phi_{N-j-1}}\, x_{N-j-1} + \tfrac{1}{2}\overline{Q_{N-j}\Delta_{N-j-1}}\, \tilde{x}_{N-j-1})$$
$$+ \tilde{x}^2_{N-j-1}(\overline{R_{N-j}} + A_{N-j}) + \tilde{x}_{N-j-1}(\overline{Q_{N-j}\phi_{N-j-1}} - 2A_{N-j}\, \overline{H\phi_{N-j-1}})x_{N-j-1}$$
$$+ \sqrt{\frac{(N-j-2)}{2K^2_{N-j}(N-j-1)}} \left[(\tilde{x}_{N-j-1} - Hx_{N-j-1})^2 + \beta_{N-j-1}v^2_{N-j-1}\right]\Big\}$$
$$\times \sqrt{\frac{N-j-1}{N-j-2}}\, K_{N-j} \prod_{i=0}^{N-j-1} \delta(x_i - \phi_{i-1}x_{i-1} - \Delta_{i-1}v_{i-1} - \Theta_{i-1}\eta_{i-1}) \prod_{i=0}^{N-j-2} p(\eta_i)$$

$$\times \left[\left(\frac{1}{\sqrt{2\pi}\sigma_w} \right)^{N-j-1} \exp \left\{ -\frac{1}{2\sigma_w^2} \sum_{i=1}^{N-j-1} (\tilde{x}_i - \tilde{x}_{i-1})^2 \right\} \right]$$

$$\times \left[\left(\frac{1}{\sqrt{2\pi}\sigma_w} \right)^{N-j-2} \exp \left\{ -a_{2,N-j-2} + \frac{2\sigma^2}{N-j-2} a_{1,N-j-2}^2 \right\} \right] d\Omega(\eta^{N-j-2}).$$

The right-hand side of Eq. (E.5) must now be minimized with respect to v_{N-j-1}. Since v_{N-j-1} appears only in the factor within braces and the rest of the expression is positive, we need only minimize this factor with respect to v_{N-j-1}. It is apparent that

$$\min_v (a + bv^2 + 2cv) = a - \frac{c^2}{b},$$

where the minimizing v equals $-c/b$. Thus, to minimize the right-hand side of Eq. (E.5), choose

$$\begin{aligned} \overline{v_{N-j-1}} = & -(x_{N-j-1}^T \overline{\phi_{N-j-1}^T P_{N-j} \Delta_{N-j-1}} - A_{N-j} \overline{H\Delta_{N-j-1}}\, \tilde{x}_{N-j-1} \\ & + A_{N-j} \overline{H\Delta_{N-j-1} H\phi_{N-j-1}}\, x_{N-j-1} + \tfrac{1}{2} \overline{Q_{N-j}\Delta_{N-j-1}}\, \tilde{x}_{N-j-1}) \\ & \times \Bigg(\overline{\Delta_{N-j-1}^T (P_{N-j} + A_{N-j} H^T H) \Delta_{N-j-1}} \\ & + \sqrt{\frac{N-j-2}{2K_{N-j}^2 (N-j-1)}}\, \beta_{N-j-1} \Bigg)^{-1}. \end{aligned} \tag{E.6}$$

The resulting minimum is given by

$$\begin{aligned} & \min_{\overline{v}_{N-j-1}} \left\{ \int \rho_{N-j}\, d\Omega(x_{N-j}, \tilde{x}_{N-j}, \xi_{N-j-1}) + \alpha_{N-j-1} \right\} \\ & = \rho_{N-j-1} \\ & = \int \Big\{ L_{N-j-1}(\xi, \eta) + x_{N-j-1}^T \overline{\phi_{N-j-1}^T (P_{N-j} + A_{N-j} H^T H) \phi_{N-j-1}}\, x_{N-j-1} \\ & \quad + \tilde{x}_{N-j-1}^2 (\overline{R_{N-j}} + A_{N-j}) + \tilde{x}_{N-j-1} (\overline{Q_{N-j}\phi_{N-j-1}} - 2A_{N-j} \overline{H\phi_{N-j-1}}) x_{N-j-1} \\ & \quad - (x_{N-j-1}^T \overline{\phi_{N-j-1}^T (P_{N-j} + A_{N-j} H^T H) \Delta_{N-j-1}} + \tilde{x}_{N-j-1} (-A_{N-j} \overline{H\Delta_{N-j-1}} \\ & \quad + \tfrac{1}{2} \overline{Q_{N-j}\Delta_{N-j-1}}))^2 \Big(\overline{\Delta_{N-j-1}^T (P_{N-j} + A_{N-j} H^T H) \Delta_{N-j-1}} \end{aligned}$$

$$+ \sqrt{\frac{N-j-2}{2K_{N-j}^2(N-j-1)}}\,\beta_{N-j-1}\Bigg)^{-1}$$

$$+ \sqrt{\frac{N-j-2}{2K_{N-j}^2(N-j-1)}}\,(\tilde{x}_{N-j-1} - Hx_{N-j-1})^2\Bigg\}$$

$$\times \sqrt{\frac{N-j-1}{N-j-2}}\,K_{N-j} \prod_{i=0}^{N-j-1} \delta(x_i - \phi_{i-1}x_{i-1} - \Delta_{i-1}v_{i-1} - \Theta_{i-1}\eta_{i-1}) \prod_{i=0}^{N-j-2} p(\eta_i)$$

$$\times \left[\left(\frac{1}{\sqrt{2\pi}\sigma_w}\right)^{N-j-1} \exp\left\{-\frac{1}{2\sigma_w{}^2} \sum_{i=1}^{N-j-1} (\tilde{x}_i - \tilde{x}_{i-1})^2\right\}\right]$$

$$\times \left[\left(\frac{1}{\sqrt{2\pi}\sigma}\right)^{N-j-2} \exp\left\{-a_{2,N-j-2} + \frac{2\sigma^2}{N-j-2}\,a_{1,N-j-2}^2\right\}\right] d\Omega(\eta^{N-j-2}).$$

This equation can be written in the following form:

$$\rho_{N-j-1} = \int \{L_{N-j-1}(\xi, \eta) + x_{N-j-1}^T P_{N-j-1} x_{N-j-1} + R_{N-j-1}\tilde{x}_{N-j-1}^2$$

$$+ Q_{N-j-1}x_{N-j-1}\tilde{x}_{N-j-1} + A_{N-j-1}(\tilde{x}_{N-j-1} - Hx_{N-j-1})^2\}K_{N-j-1}$$

$$\times \prod_{i=0}^{N-j-1} \delta(x_i - \phi_{i-1}x_{i-1} - \Delta_{i-1}v_{i-1} - \Theta_{i-1}\eta_{i-1}) \prod_{i=0}^{N-j-2} p(\eta_i)$$

$$\times \left[\left(\frac{1}{\sqrt{2\pi}\sigma_w}\right)^{N-j-1} \exp\left\{-\frac{1}{2\sigma_w{}^2} \sum_{i=1}^{N-j-1} (\tilde{x}_i - \tilde{x}_{i-1})^2\right\}\right]$$

$$\times \left[\left(\frac{1}{\sqrt{2\pi}\sigma}\right)^{N-j-2} \exp\left\{-a_{2,N-j-2} + \frac{2\sigma^2}{N-j-2}\,a_{1,N-j-2}^2\right\}\right] d\Omega(\eta^{N-j-2}),$$

where the following definitions are used:

$$K_{N-j-1} = \sqrt{\frac{N-j-1}{N-j-2}}\,K_{N-j}\,,$$

$$A_{N-j-1} = \sqrt{\frac{N-j-2}{2(N-j-1)}}\,\frac{1}{K_{N-j}}\,,$$

$$P_{N-j-1} = \overline{\phi^T_{N-j-1}(P_{N-j} + A_{N-j}H^TH)\phi_{N-j-1}}$$
$$- (M_{N-j-1})^{-1}\,\overline{\phi^T_{N-j-1}(P_{N-j} + A_{N-j}H^TH)\Delta_{N-j-1}}$$
$$\times\, \overline{\Delta^T_{N-j-1}(P_{N-j} + A_{N-j}H^TH)^T\phi_{N-j-1}}\,,$$

$$Q_{N-j-1} = \overline{Q_{N-j}\phi_{N-j-1}} - 2A_{N-j}\overline{H\phi_{N-j-1}} - 2(-A_{N-j}\overline{H\Delta_{N-j-1}} + \tfrac{1}{2}\overline{Q_{N-j}\Delta_{N-j-1}}) \tag{E.7}$$
$$\times\, (\overline{\Delta^T_{N-j-1}(P_{N-j} + A_{N-j}H^TH)^T\phi_{N-j-1}})(M_{N-j-1})^{-1},$$

$$R_{N-j-1} = \overline{R_{N-j}} + A_{N-j} - (-A_{N-j}\overline{H\Delta_{N-j-1}} + \tfrac{1}{2}\overline{Q_{N-j}\Delta_{N-j-1}})^2(M_{N-j-1})^{-1},$$

$$M_{N-j-1} = \overline{\Delta^T_{N-j-1}(P_{N-j} + A_{N-j}H^TH)\Delta_{N-j-1}} + \frac{N-j-2}{2K^2_{N-j}(N-j-1)}\,\beta_{N-j-1}.$$

If we use the values given in Eq. (5.11) as initial values for these recurrence formulas we obtain the result that:

$$K_{N-j-1} = \sqrt{\frac{N}{2(N-j-2)}}\,,$$

$$A_{N-j-1} = \sqrt{\frac{N-j-2}{N}}\,,$$

$$P_{N-j-1} = \overline{\phi^T_{N-j-1}\left(P_{N-j} + \sqrt{\frac{N-j-1}{N}}\,H^TH\right)\phi_{N-j-1}}$$
$$- (M_{N-j-1})^{-1}\,\overline{\phi^T_{N-j-1}\left(P_{N-j} + \sqrt{\frac{N-j-1}{N}}\,H^TH\right)\Delta_{N-j-1}}$$
$$\times\, \overline{\Delta^T_{N-j-1}\left(P_{N-j} + \sqrt{\frac{N-j-1}{N}}\,H^TH\right)^T\phi_{N-j-1}}\,, \tag{E.8}$$

$$Q_{N-j-1} = \overline{Q_{N-j}\phi_{N-j-1}} - 2\sqrt{\frac{N-j-1}{N}}\,\overline{H\phi_{N-j-1}}$$
$$- 2\left(-\sqrt{\frac{N-j-2}{N}}\,\overline{H\Delta_{N-j-1}} + \tfrac{1}{2}\overline{Q_{N-j}\Delta_{N-j-1}}\right)$$
$$\times\, \overline{\Delta^T_{N-j-1}\left(P_{N-j} + \sqrt{\frac{N-j-1}{N}}\,H^TH\right)^T\phi_{N-j-1}}\,(M_{N-j-1})^{-1},$$

$$R_{N-j-1} = \overline{R_{N-j}} + \sqrt{\frac{N-j-1}{N}}$$
$$- (-A_{N-j}\overline{H\Delta_{N-j-1}} + \tfrac{1}{2}\overline{Q_{N-j}\Delta_{N-j-1}})^2(M_{N-j-1})^{-1},$$

$$M_{N-j-1} = \overline{\Delta^T_{N-j-1}\left(P_{N-j} + \sqrt{\frac{N-j-1}{N}}\, H^TH\right)\Delta_{N-j-1}}$$
$$+ \sqrt{\frac{N-j-2}{N}}\,\beta_{N-j-1},$$

$$L_{N-j-1} = \overline{\hat{L}_{N-j}(\xi, N)} + \sigma_\lambda{}^2\, \overline{\Theta^T_{N-j-1}\left(P_{N-j} + \sqrt{\frac{N-j-1}{N}}\, H^TH\right)\Theta_{N-j}}$$
$$+ \sigma_w{}^2\left(\overline{R_{N-j}} + \sqrt{\frac{N-j-1}{N}}\right).$$

Let us note in passing that Eq. (E.5) can be written as:

$$\int \rho_{N-j}\, d\Omega(x_{N-j}, \tilde{x}_{N-j}, \xi_{N-j-1}) + \alpha_{N-j-1}$$
$$= K_{N-j-1}\int \{L_{N-j-1}(\xi, \eta) + x^T_{N-j-1}P_{N-j-1}x_{N-j-1} + R_{N-j-1}\tilde{x}^2_{N-j-1}$$
$$+ Q_{N-j-1}x_{N-j-1}\tilde{x}_{N-j-1} + A_{N-j-1}(\tilde{x}_{N-j-1} - Hx_{N-j-1})^2$$
$$+ M_{N-j-1}(v_{N-j-1} + [x^T_{T-j-1}\,\overline{\Phi^T_{N-j-1}P_{N-j}\Delta_{N-j-1}} - A_{N-j}\,\overline{H\Delta_{N-j-1}}\,\tilde{x}_{N-j-1}$$
$$+ A_{N-j}\,\overline{H\Delta_{N-j-1}H\Phi_{N-j-1}}\,x_{N-j-1} + \tfrac{1}{2}\,\overline{Q_{N-j}\Delta_{N-j-1}}\,\tilde{x}_{N-j-1}]M^{-1}_{N-j-1})^2\}$$
$$\times \prod_{i=0}^{N-j-1}\delta_i \prod_{i=0}^{N-j-2} p(\eta_i) \prod_{i=0}^{N-j-1} p(\tilde{x}_i \mid \tilde{x}_{i-1})$$
$$\times\left[\left(\frac{1}{\sqrt{2\pi}\sigma}\right)^{N-j-2}\exp\{a_{N-j-1}\} + O\left(\frac{1}{\sqrt{n}}\right)\right] d\Omega(\eta^{N-j-2}). \tag{E.9}$$

In Eq. (E.9) the quadratic nature of the criterion is more obvious than is the case with Eq. (E.5). The recurrence formula for P_j and M_j takes on a simpler form if we define the matrix B_j by the relation

$$B_{N-j-1} = P_{N-j} + \sqrt{\frac{N-j-1}{N}}\, H^TH.$$

Then,

$$P_{N-j-1} = \overline{\Phi^T_{N-j-1} B_{N-j-1} \Phi_{N-j-1}} - (M_{N-j-1})^{-1} \overline{\Phi^T_{N-j-1} B_{N-j-1} \Delta_{N-j-1}} \times \overline{\Delta^T_{N-j-1} B^T_{N-j-1} \Phi_{N-j-1}},$$

and

$$M_{N-j-1} = \overline{\Delta^T_{N-j-1} B_{N-j-1} \Delta_{N-j-1}} + \sqrt{\frac{N-j-2}{N}} \beta_{N-j-2}.$$

Appendix F

In this appendix we will develop some of the properties of an adaptive control system described by a set of equations of the following form.

1. Plant equation:

$$z_s + \sum_{i=1}^{n} (\alpha_s{}^i + \beta_s{}^i \xi_s) z_{s-i} = v_{s-1} + \gamma_{s-1}, \qquad 1 \leqslant s \leqslant N,$$

where

$$\begin{aligned} \beta_s{}^i &= \beta_s{}^k, \qquad i = k, \quad 1 \leqslant s \leqslant N, \\ &= 0, \qquad\; i \neq k, \quad 1 \leqslant s \leqslant N. \end{aligned}$$

2. Input equation given by Eq. (5.4).
3. Performance index:

$$h(\tilde{x}^N, z^N, \bar{v}) = \sum_{i=q}^{N} (\tilde{x}_s - z_s)^2 + v_N{}^2.$$

The plant equation can be written as

$$x_s = (\phi_{1,s} + \xi\phi_{2,s}) x_{s-1} + \Delta v_{s-1} + \Theta\gamma_{s-1},$$

where

$$x_s = \begin{bmatrix} z_{s-n+1} \\ \vdots \\ \\ z_s \end{bmatrix}, \qquad \Delta = \begin{bmatrix} 0 \\ \vdots \\ 0 \\ 1 \end{bmatrix}, \qquad \Theta = \begin{bmatrix} 0 \\ \vdots \\ 0 \\ 1 \end{bmatrix} \tag{F.1}$$

$$\phi_{1,s} = \begin{bmatrix} 0 & 1 & 0 & \cdots & 0 \\ 0 & 0 & 1 & \cdots & 0 \\ \vdots & & & & \\ 0 & & & \cdots & 1 \\ -\alpha_s{}^n & & & \cdots & -\alpha_s{}^1 \end{bmatrix} \qquad \phi_{2,s} = \begin{bmatrix} 0 & 0 & 0 & \cdots & 0 \\ 0 & 0 & 0 & \cdots & 0 \\ \vdots & \vdots & & & \\ 0 & 0 & & \cdots & 0 \\ 0 & -\beta_s{}^k & 0 & \cdots & 0 \end{bmatrix}$$

The output is Hx_s where H is given by

$$H = [0, \ldots, 0, 1]. \tag{F.2}$$

For a process of this type the recurrence formula which the optimal control must satisfy is simplified by the circumstance that the weighting of the control action occurs only when $j = N$. From Eq. (F.1), it is apparent that $H\Delta_{N-j-1} \equiv 1$. Thus, defining ϕ by the equation

$$\phi = \phi_{1s} + \phi_{2s}\xi,$$

we obtain

$$\begin{aligned}
P_{N-j-1} &= \overline{\phi^T_{N-j-1} P_{N-j} \phi_{N-j-1}} + A_{N-j}\overline{\phi^T_{N-j-1} H^T H \phi_{N-j-1}} \\
&\quad - \frac{(\overline{\phi^T_{N-j-1}P_{N-j}}\,\Delta + A_{N-j}\overline{\phi^T_{N-j-1}}H^T)(\overline{\phi^T_{N-j-1}P_{N-j}}\,\Delta + A_{N-j}\overline{\phi^T_{N-j-1}}H^T)^T}{M_{N-j}} \\
Q_{N-j-1} &= \overline{Q_{N-j}\phi_{N-j-1}} - 2A_{N-j}H\overline{\phi_{N-j-1}} \\
&\quad + \frac{-2(\overline{\phi^T_{N-j-1}P_{N-j}}\,\Delta + A_{N-j}\overline{\phi^T_{N-j-1}}H^T)^T(\tfrac{1}{2}\overline{Q_{N-j}}\,\Delta - A_{N-j})}{M_{N-j}}, \qquad \text{(F.3)} \\
R_{N-j-1} &= \overline{R_{N-j}} + A_{N-j} - \frac{(\tfrac{1}{2}\overline{Q_{N-j}}\,\Delta - A_{N-j})(\tfrac{1}{2}\overline{Q_{N-j}}\,\Delta - A_{N-j})}{M_{N-j}}, \\
M_{N-j} &= \Delta^T\overline{P_{N-j}}\,\Delta + A_{N-j}\,.
\end{aligned}$$

To show that the control policy given by Eq. (5.17) is minimax, it would be useful to be able to show that it is an equalizer. For this purpose let us prove the following matrix product result. The notation $(M)_{ij}$ will be used to represent the element of the matrix M in row i and column j.

RESULT 1. Let A, B, and D be $n \times n$ matrices with elements a_{ij}, b_{ij}, and c_{ij} such that

$$\begin{aligned}
a_{ij} &= 0, && i < n \quad \text{and} \quad j \neq i + 1, \\
&= \alpha_{ij} && \text{otherwise}, \\
b_{ij} &= 0, && i < n, \\
&= \beta_{ij} && \text{otherwise}, \\
d_{ij} &= 0, && i \neq j, \\
&= \delta_{ij}\,, && i = j \neq n, \\
&= 0, && i = j = n.
\end{aligned}$$

Then,

(a) A^TDA is diagonal
(b) $A^TDB = B^TDA = 0$
(c) $B^TDB = 0$.

Proof. (a) For any three $n \times n$ matrices it is true that

$$(MNQ)_{ij} = \sum_{k=1}^{n} \sum_{l=1}^{n} (M)_{ik}(N)_{kl}(Q)_{lj} .$$

Since D is diagonal

$$\begin{aligned}(A^TDA)_{ij} &= \sum_{k=1}^{n-1} a_{ki}d_{kk}a_{kj} \\ &= 0 \qquad \text{if} \quad i \neq j, \\ &= \alpha_{i-1,i}^2 \delta_{i-1,i-1} , \qquad i = j,\end{aligned}$$

where $\delta_{-1,-1} = \alpha_{-1,1} = 0$. Thus, A^TDA is diagonal.

(b) In a similar manner

$$\begin{aligned}(A^TDB)_{ij} &= \sum_{k=1}^{n} \sum_{l=1}^{n} a_{ki}d_{lk}b_{lj} \\ &= \sum_{k=1}^{n-1} a_{ki}d_{kk}b_{kj} .\end{aligned}$$

But $b_{kj} = 0$ for $k < n$. Thus,

$$(A^TDB)_{ij} = 0,$$

and therefore,

$$(A^TDB)^T = B^TDA = 0.$$

(c) Finally,

$$\begin{aligned}(B^TDB)_{ij} &= \sum_{k=1}^{n-1} b_{ki}d_{kk}b_{kj} \\ &= 0. \quad \blacktriangledown\end{aligned}$$

Let us next prove a second matrix product result.

RESULT 2. Let the $n \times 1$ matrices Δ and H be defined by Eqs. (F.1) and (F.2) and let P be an $n \times n$ diagonal matrix with elements p_{ii}. Then,

$$D_1 = P\Delta^T P\Delta - P\Delta\Delta^T P$$

and

$$D_2 = H^T H\Delta^T P\Delta + P - 2H^T H\Delta^T P\Delta$$

are $n \times n$ diagonal matrices with the property

$$(D_1)_{nn} = (D_2)_{nn} = 0.$$

Proof. Consider D_1 first. $\Delta^T P\Delta = p_{nn}$. Thus, $P\Delta^T P\Delta = p_{nn}P$. Also $P\Delta = p_{nn}\Delta$ and $\Delta^T P = p_{nn}\Delta^T$. Consequently, we have $P\Delta\Delta^T P = p_{nn}^2 \Delta\Delta^T$ or

$$\begin{aligned}(P\Delta\Delta^T P)_{ij} &= p_{nn}^2, \qquad && i = j = n,\\ &= 0 && \text{otherwise.}\end{aligned}$$

Combining the two matrix products,

$$\begin{aligned}(P\Delta^T P\Delta - P\Delta\Delta^T P)_{ij} &= 0, \qquad && i \neq j,\\ &= p_{ii}p_{nn}, && i = j \neq n,\\ &= 0, && i = j = n.\end{aligned}$$

Next consider D_2. Since $\Delta^T P\Delta = p_{nn}$,

$$\begin{aligned}(H^T H\Delta^T P\Delta)_{ij} &= p_{nn}, \qquad && i = j = n,\\ &= 0 && \text{otherwise.}\end{aligned}$$

Therefore,

$$\begin{aligned}(H^T H\Delta^T P\Delta + P - 2H^T H\Delta^T P\Delta)_{ij} &= 0, \qquad && i \neq j,\\ &= 2p_{ii}, && i = j \neq n,\\ &= 0, && i = j = n.\end{aligned}$$

We thus have the result that D_1 and D_2 are diagonal with $(D_1)_{nn} = (D_2)_{nn} = 0$. ▼

We can now use Results 1 and 2 to prove that P_j, Q_j, and R_j are independent of ξ^N. First consider P_j.

RESULT 3. If P_i satisfies the recurrence formula given by Eq. (F.3) and if P_{N-j} for $j < N-2$ is diagonal and independent of ξ^N, then P_{N-j-1} is diagonal and independent of ξ^N.

Proof. Using Eq. (F.3), and the fact that P_{N-j} is diagonal and independent of ξ^N, we have

$$\begin{aligned}P_{N-j-1} = {} & \phi_{1,N-j-1}^T P_{N-j} \phi_{1,N-j-1} \\ & + \overline{\xi_{N-j-1}} (\phi_{1,N-j-1}^T P_{N-j} \phi_{2,N-j-1} + \phi_{2,N-j-1}^T P_{N-j} \phi_{1,N-j-1}) \\ & + \overline{\xi_{N-j-1}^2} (\phi_{2,N-j-1}^T P_{N-j} \phi_{2,N-j-1}) + A_{N-j} \{ \phi_{1,N-j-1}^T H^T H \phi_{1,N-j-1} \\ & + \overline{\xi_{N-j-1}} (\phi_{2,N-j-1}^T H^T H \phi_{1,N-j-1} + \phi_{1,N-j-1}^T H^T H \phi_{2,N-j-1}) \\ & + \overline{\xi_{N-j-1}^2} \phi_{2,N-j-1}^T H^T H \phi_{2,N-j-1} \} \\ & - \frac{(\phi_{1,N-j-1} + \phi_{2,N-j-1} \overline{\xi_{N-j-1}})^T (P_{N-j} \Delta \Delta^T P_{N-j}}{\Delta^T P_{N-j} \Delta + A_{N-j}} \\ & + \frac{A_{N-j}^2 H^T H + 2 A_{N-j} H^T \Delta^T P_{N-j}) (\phi_{1,N-j-1} + \phi_{2,N-j-1} \overline{\xi_{N-j-1}})}{\Delta^T P_{N-j} \Delta + A_{N-j}} .\end{aligned}$$

This can be written as

$$\begin{aligned}& (\Delta^T P_{N-j} \Delta + A_{N-j}) P_{N-j-1} \\ & \quad = \phi_{1,N-j-1}^T T_{N-j} \phi_{1,N-j-1} + \phi_{1,N-j-1}^T T_{N-j} \phi_{2,N-j-1} \overline{\xi_{N-j-1}} \\ & \quad\quad + \phi_{2,N-j-1}^T T_{N-j} \phi_{1,N-j-1} \overline{\xi_{N-j-1}} + \phi_{2\ N-j-1}^T \\ & \quad\quad \times \{ P_{N-j} \Delta^T P_{N-j} \Delta + A_{N-j} (H^T H \Delta^T P_{N-j} \Delta + P_{N-j}) + A_{N-j}^2 H^T H \} \phi_{2,N-j-1} \\ & \quad\quad \times \overline{\xi_{N-j-1}^2} - \phi_{2,N-j-1}^T \{ P_{N-j} \Delta \Delta^T P_{N-j} + A_{N-j}^2 H^T H + 2 A_{N-j} H^T \Delta^T P_{N-j} \} \\ & \quad\quad \times \phi_{2,N-j-1} (\overline{\xi_{N-j-1}})^2 ,\end{aligned}$$

where

$$\begin{aligned}T_{N-j} = {} & P_{N-j} \Delta^T P_{N-j} \Delta - P_{N-j} \Delta \Delta^T P_{N-j} \\ & + A_{N-j} (H^T H \Delta^T P_{N-j} \Delta + P_{N-j} - 2 H^T \Delta^T P_{N-j}).\end{aligned}$$

From Eq. (F.1) it is clear that $\phi_{1,N-j-1}$ corresponds to the matrix A in Result 1 and $\phi_{2,N-j-1}$ corresponds to the matrix B. Result 2 can be used directly to show that T_{N-j} is diagonal and $(T_{N-j})_{nn} = 0$. Therefore, by Result 1,

(a) $\phi_{1,N-j-1}^T T_{N-j} \phi_{1,N-j-1}$ is diagonal, and

(b) $\phi_{2,N-j-1}^T T_{N-j} \phi_{1,N-j-1} = \phi_{1,N-j-1}^T T_{N-j} \phi_{2,N-j-1} = 0$.

This permits some some simplification in the expression for P_{N-j-1}.

$$\begin{aligned}
(\Delta^T P_{N-j} \Delta + A_{N-j}) P_{N-j-1} \\
&= [\overline{\xi_{N-j-1}^2} - (\overline{\xi_{N-j-1}})^2] \phi_{2,N-j-1}^T \\
&\quad \times \{P_{N-j}\Delta^T P_{N-j}\Delta^T + A_{N-j}(H^T H \Delta^T P_{N-j}\Delta + P_{N-j}) + A_{N-j}^2 H^T H\} \phi_{2,N-j-1} \\
&\quad - \phi_{2,N-j-1} T_{N-j} \phi_{2,N-j-1} (\overline{\xi_{N-j-1}})^2 + \phi_{1,N-j-1}^T T_{N-j} \phi_{1,N-j-1}.
\end{aligned}$$

Using the third conclusion in Result 1, it is clear that

$$\phi_{2,N-j-1} T_{N-j} \phi_{2,N-j-1} = 0.$$

By definition, if $j < N - 2$,

$$\begin{aligned}
\overline{\xi_{N-j-1}^2} &= \sqrt{\frac{N-j-2}{2(N-j-1)\pi\sigma^2}} \int_{-\infty}^{\infty} \xi_{N-j-1}^2 \exp\Bigg[-\frac{1}{2\sigma^2}\frac{N-j-2}{N-j-1} \\
&\quad \times \left(\xi_{N-j-1} - \xi_{N-j-2} - \frac{1}{N-j-2}\sum_{i=1}^{N-j-2}(\xi_i - \xi_{i-1})\right)^2\Bigg] d\xi_{N-j-1} \\
&= \frac{N-j-1}{N-j-2}\sigma^2 + \left(\xi_{N-j-2} + \frac{1}{N-j-2}\sum_{i=1}^{N-j-2}(\xi_i - \xi_{i-1})\right)^2,
\end{aligned}$$

$$\begin{aligned}
(\overline{\xi_{N-j-1}})^2 &= \sqrt{\frac{N-j-2}{2(N-j-1)\pi\sigma^2}} \Bigg\{\int_{-\infty}^{\infty} \xi_{N-j-1} \exp\Bigg[-\frac{1}{2\sigma^2}\frac{N-j-2}{N-j-1} \\
&\quad \times \left(\xi_{N-j-1} - \xi_{N-j-2} - \frac{1}{N-j-2}\sum_{i=1}^{N-j-2}(\xi_i - \xi_{i-1})\right)^2\Bigg] d\xi_{N-j-1}\Bigg\}^2 \\
&= \left(\xi_{N-j-2} + \frac{1}{N-j-2}\sum_{i=1}^{N-j-2}(\xi_i - \xi_{i-1})\right)^2.
\end{aligned}$$

Therefore,

$$\overline{\xi^2_{N-j-1}} - (\overline{\xi_{N-j-1}})^2 = \frac{N-j-1}{N-j-2}\,\sigma^2. \tag{F.4}$$

A slight amount of algebra will convince the reader that

$$\begin{aligned}(P_{N-j}\Delta^T P_{N-j}\Delta + A_{N-j}(H^T H\Delta^T P_{N-j}\Delta + P_{N-j}) + A^2_{N-j}H^T H)_{ij}\\ &= 0, && i \neq j,\\ &= A_{N-j}p_{ii}, && i = j \neq n,\\ &= p_{nn}(1 + 2A_{N-j}) + A^2_{N-j}, && i = j = n.\end{aligned}$$

If we expand the following matrix product, we will obtain

$$\begin{aligned}(\phi^T_{2,N-j-1}\{P_{N-j}\Delta^T P_{N-j}\Delta + A_{N-j}(H^T H\Delta^T P_{N-j}\Delta + P_{N-j}) + A^2_{N-j}H^T H\}\phi_{2,N-j-1})_{ij}\\ &= 0, && i \neq j,\\ &= 0, && i = j \neq k,\\ &= (\beta^k_{N-j-1})^2 p_{nn}(1 + 2A_{N-j}) + A^2_{N-j}, && i = j = k.\end{aligned}$$

All of the above factors are independent of ξ^N. Combining our equations, we have

$$\begin{aligned}P_{N-j-1} = \frac{N-j-1}{N-j-2}\,\sigma^2\phi^T_{2,N-j-1}\{P_{N-j}\Delta^T P_{N-j}\Delta + A_{N-j}(H^T H\Delta^T P_{N-j}\Delta + P_{N-j})\\ + A^2_{N-j}H^T H\}\phi_{2,N-j-1} + \phi^T_{1,N-j-1}T_{N-j}\phi_{1,N-j-1}.\end{aligned}$$

Consequently, P_{N-j-1} is diagonal and independent of ξ^N. ▼

RESULT 4. If Q_i and R_i satisfy the recurrence formula given by Eq. (F.3), if P_{N-j} is diagonal and independent of ξ^N, if $Q_{N-j} = 0$, and if R_{N-j} is independent of ξ^N, then $Q_{N-j-1} = 0$ and R_{N-j-1} is independent of ξ^N.

Proof. Let us first treat Q_{N-j-1}. If $Q_{N-j} = 0$,

$$\begin{aligned}\left(\Delta^T P_{N-j}\Delta + \sqrt{\frac{N-j-1}{N}}\right) Q_{N-j-1}\\ &= -2A_{N-j}\{H\overline{\phi_{N-j-1}}(\Delta^T P_{N-j}\Delta + A_{N-j}) - (\Delta^T P_{N-j}\overline{\phi_{N-j-1}} + A_{N-j}H\overline{\phi_{N-j-1}})\}\\ &= -2A_{N-j}\{H\Delta^T P_{N-j}\Delta - \Delta^T P_{N-j}\}\overline{\phi_{N-j-1}}.\end{aligned}$$

But $H\Delta^T P_{N-j}\Delta = p_{nn}H = p_{nn}\Delta^T = \Delta^T P_{N-j}$. Therefore,

$$Q_{N-j-1} = 0.$$

The proof that R_{N-j-1} is independent of ξ^N is immediate from Eq. (F.3) since nothing on the right side of the equation defining R_{N-j-1} depends on ξ^N. ▼

Appendix G

In this appendix we shall show explicitly the derivation of Eq. (6.15). If Eq. (6.14) is substituted into the equation for ρ_{N-1}, we obtain

$$\rho_{N-1} = \left(\frac{1}{\sqrt{2\pi}\sigma}\right)^{N-1} \Bigg[\Bigg\{2\sigma_1^2 + \sigma^2 + y_{N-1}^2 \times \left(1 + a^2\left[1 - \frac{\theta_1(\theta_1 p \Sigma_1^{N-1} + \theta_2 q \Sigma_2^{N-1})}{p\theta_1^2 \Sigma_1^{N-1} + q\theta_2^2 \Sigma_2^{N-1}}\right]^2\right)\Bigg\} p\Sigma_1^{N-1}$$

$$+ \Bigg\{2\sigma_1^2 + \sigma^2 + y_{N-1}^2\left(1 + a^2\left[1 - \frac{\theta_2(\theta_1 p \Sigma_1^{N-1} + \theta_2 q \Sigma_2^{N-1})}{p\theta_1^2 \Sigma_1^{N-1} + q\theta_2^2 \Sigma_2^{N-1}}\right]^2\right)\Bigg\} q\Sigma_2^{N-1}\Bigg].$$

Let us consider the following terms:

$$\left[1 - \frac{\theta_1(\theta_1 p \Sigma_1^{N-1} + \theta_2 q \Sigma_2^{N-1})}{\theta_1^2 p \Sigma_1^{N-1} + \theta_2^2 q \Sigma_2^{N-1}}\right]^2 p\Sigma_1^{N-1} + \left[1 - \frac{\theta_2(\theta_1 p \Sigma_1^{N-1} + \theta_2 q \Sigma_2^{N-1})}{p\theta_1^2 \Sigma_1^{N-1} + \theta_2^2 q \Sigma_2^{N-1}}\right]^2 q\Sigma_2^{N-1}$$

$$= \frac{(\theta_2^2 q \Sigma_2^{N-1} - \theta_1\theta_2 q \Sigma_2^{N-1})^2 p \Sigma_1^{N-1} + (p\theta_1^2 \Sigma_1^{N-1} - \theta_1\theta_2 p \Sigma_1^{N-1})^2 q \Sigma_2^{N-1}}{(\theta_1^2 p \Sigma_1^{N-1} + \theta_2^2 q \Sigma_2^{N-1})^2}$$

$$= pq\Sigma_1^{N-1}\Sigma_2^{N-1}(\theta_2^4 q \Sigma_2^{N-1} - 2\theta_1\theta_2^3 q \Sigma_2^{N-1} + \theta_1^2\theta_2^2 q \Sigma_2^{N-1} + \theta_1^4 p \Sigma_1^{N-1}$$

$$- 2\theta_1^3\theta_2 p \Sigma_1^{N-1} + \theta_1^2\theta_2^2 p \Sigma_1^{N-1}) \frac{1}{(\theta_1^2 p \Sigma_1^{N-1} + \theta_2^2 q \Sigma_2^{N-1})^2}$$

$$= \frac{pq\Sigma_1^{N-1}\Sigma_2^{N-1}(\theta_2 - \theta_1)^2}{\theta_1^2 p \Sigma_1^{N-1} + \theta_2^2 q \Sigma_2^{N-1}}.$$

If the above identity is substituted into Eq. (6.15), we find that

$$\rho_{N-1} = \left(\frac{1}{\sqrt{2\pi}\sigma}\right)^{N-1} \Bigg[(2\sigma_1^2 + \sigma^2 + y_{N-1}^2) p\Sigma_1^{N-1} + (2\sigma_1^2 + \sigma^2 + y_{N-1}^2) q\Sigma_2^{N-1}$$

$$+ a^2 y_{N-1}^2 \frac{pq(\theta_2 - \theta_1)^2 \Sigma_1^{N-1}\Sigma_2^{N-1}}{\theta_1^2 p \Sigma_1^{N-1} + \theta_2^2 q \Sigma_2^{N-1}}\Bigg].$$

Appendix H

In this appendix we will treat some of the limit properties of the recurrence formula for the Bayes control policy. Let us assume that

$$\rho_{N-j} = \left(\frac{1}{\sqrt{2\pi}\sigma}\right)^{N-j} \left[(\sigma_{3,N-j}^2 + a_{N-j}y_{N-j}^2)p\Sigma_1^{N-j} + (\sigma_{4,N-j}^2 + b_{N-j}y_{N-j}^2)q\Sigma_1^{N-j}\right].$$

From Eq. (6.12) it is evident that ρ_N has this form, so the necessary initial values for a recurrence formula are available. Integrating ρ_{N-j} with respect to y_{N-j}, we have

$$\begin{aligned}
&\int \rho_{N-j}\, d\Omega(y_{N-j}) \\
&\quad = \left(\frac{1}{\sqrt{2\pi}\sigma}\right)^{N-j} \left[p\Sigma_1^{N-j-1} \int_{-\infty}^{\infty} (\sigma_{3,N-j}^2 + a_{N-j}y_{N-j}^2)\right. \\
&\qquad \times \exp - \left\{\frac{(y_{N-j} - ay_{N-j-1} - \theta_1 v_{N-j-1})^2}{2\sigma^2}\right\} dy_{N-j} \\
&\qquad + q\Sigma_2^{N-j-1} \int_{-\infty}^{\infty} (\sigma_{4,N-j}^2 + b_{N-j}y_{N-j}^2) \\
&\qquad \left. \times \exp\left\{-\frac{(y_{N-j} - ay_{N-j-1} - \theta_2 v_{N-j-1})^2}{2\sigma^2}\right\} dy_{N-j}\right] \\
&\quad = \left(\frac{1}{\sqrt{2\pi}\sigma}\right)^{N-j-1} [p\Sigma_1^{N-j-1}[\sigma_{3,N-j}^2 + a_{N-j}(\sigma^2 + (ay_{N-j-1} + \theta_1 v_{N-j-1})^2] \\
&\qquad + q\Sigma_2^{N-j-1}[\sigma_{4,N-j}^2 + b_{N-j}(\sigma^2 + (ay_{N-j-1} + \theta_2 v_{N-j-1})^2]].
\end{aligned}$$

Performing the integration indicated in Eq. (6.11), we have

$$\alpha_{N-j-1} = \left(\frac{1}{\sqrt{2\pi}\sigma}\right)^{N-j-1} ({\sigma_1}^2 + y_{N-j-1}^2)[p\Sigma_1^{N-j-1} + q\Sigma_2^{N-j-1}].$$

Thus, we have

$$\alpha_{N-j-1} + \int \rho_{N-j}\, d\Omega(y_{N-j})$$
$$= \left(\frac{1}{\sqrt{2\pi}\sigma}\right)^{N-j-1} [(\sigma^2_{3,N-j} + a_{N-j}\sigma^2 + \sigma_1{}^2 + y^2_{N-j-1}$$
$$+ a_{N-j}(ay_{N-j-1} + \theta_1 v_{N-j-1})^2)$$
$$\times p\Sigma_1^{N-j-1} + (\sigma^2_{4,N-j} + b_{N-j}\sigma^2 + \sigma_1{}^2 + y^2_{N-j-1}$$
$$+ b_{N-j}(ay_{N-j-1} + \theta_2 v_{N-j-1})^2)q\Sigma_2^{N-j-1}]. \tag{H.1}$$

By definition

$$\rho_{N-j-1} = \min_{\bar{v}_{N-j-1}} \left\{\alpha_{N-j-1} + \int \rho_{N-j}\, d\Omega(y_{N-j})\right\}.$$

The minimum will be achieved when $\bar{v}_{N-j-1}$ is chosen such that

$$a_{N-j}\theta_1(ay_{N-j-1} + \theta_1 v_{N-j-1})p\Sigma_1^{N-j-1} + b_{N-j}\theta_2(ay_{N-j-1} + \theta_2 v_{N-j-1})q\Sigma_2^{N-j-1} = 0.$$

Solving this equation for the minimizing $\bar{v}_{N-j-1}$, we have

$$(\bar{v}_{N-j-1})_{\min} = -ay_{N-j-1}\frac{a_{N-j}\theta_1 p\Sigma_1^{N-j-1} + b_{N-j}\theta_2 q\Sigma_2^{N-j-1}}{a_{N-j}\theta_1{}^2 p\Sigma_1^{N-j-1} + b_{N-j}\theta_2{}^2 q\Sigma_2^{N-j-1}}. \tag{H.2}$$

Define

$$\sigma^2_{3,N-j-1} = \sigma^2_{3,N-j} + a_{N-j}\sigma^2 + \sigma_1{}^2,$$

and

$$\sigma^2_{4,N-j-1} = \sigma^2_{4,N-j} + b_{N-j}\sigma^2 + \sigma_1{}^2. \tag{H.3}$$

Substituting Eqs. (H.2) and (H.3) into (H.1), we obtain:

$$\rho_{N-j-1} = \left(\frac{1}{\sqrt{2\pi}\sigma}\right)^{N-j-1}\Bigg[\Bigg\{\sigma^2_{3,N-j-1} + y^2_{N-j-1} + a_{N-j}a^2y^2_{N-j}$$
$$\times\left(1 - \frac{\theta_1(a_{N-j}\theta_1 p\Sigma_1^{N-j-1} + b_{N-j}\theta_2 q\Sigma_2^{N-j-1})}{a_{N-j}\theta_1{}^2 p\Sigma_1^{N-j-1} + b_{N-j}\theta_2{}^2 q\Sigma_2^{N-j-1}}\right)\Bigg\}$$
$$\times p\Sigma_1^{N-j-1} + \Bigg(\sigma^2_{4,N-j-1} + y^2_{N-j-1} + b_{N-j}a^2y^2_{N-j-1}$$
$$\times\left(1 - \frac{\theta_2(a_{N-j}\theta_1 p\Sigma_1^{N-j-1} + b_{N-j}\theta_2 q\Sigma_2^{N-j-1})}{a_{N-j}\theta_1{}^2 p\Sigma_1^{N-j-1} + b_{N-j}\theta_2{}^2 q\Sigma_2^{N-j-1}}\right)^2\Bigg) q\Sigma_2^{N-j-1}\Bigg].$$

Using the same technique of combining terms that was indicated in Appendix G, one can show that

$$\rho_{N-j-1} = \left(\frac{1}{\sqrt{2\pi}\sigma}\right)^{N-j-1} \Bigg[(\sigma_{3,N-j-1}^2 + y_{N-j-1}^2)p\Sigma_1^{N-j-1} + (\sigma_{4,N-j-1}^2 + y_{N-j-1}^2)q\Sigma_2^{N-j-1} + a^2y_{N-j-1}^2 \frac{pqa_{N-j}b_{N-j}\Sigma_1^{N-j-1}\Sigma_2^{N-j-1}(\theta_2-\theta_1)^2}{a_{N-j}\theta_1^{\,2}p\Sigma_1^{N-j-1} + b_{N-j}\theta_2^{\,2}q\Sigma_2^{N-j-1}}\Bigg]. \tag{H.4}$$

At this point we encounter the same problem that was experienced in the analysis of Eq. (6.15). Because of the form of the last term, $\int \rho_{N-j-1}$ cannot be evaluated directly. Since we cannot deal with the integral in full generality, let us examine some special forms of Eq. (H.4).

CASE 1. Let us assume that

$$\frac{a_{N-j}\theta_1^{\,2}\Sigma_1^{N-j-1}}{b_{N-j}\theta_2^{\,2}q\Sigma_2^{N-j-1}} > 1.$$

Then, if only first-order terms are retained,

$$\frac{1}{a_{N-j}\theta_1^{\,2}p\Sigma_1^{N-j-1} + b_{N-j}\theta_2^{\,2}\Sigma_2^{N-j-1}} \sim \frac{1 - b_{N-j}\theta_2^{\,2}q\Sigma_2^{N-j-1}/a_{N-j}\theta_1^{\,2}p\Sigma_1^{N-j-1}}{a_{N-j}\theta_1^{\,2}p\Sigma_1^{N-j-1}}.$$

and therefore,

$$\frac{pqa_{N-j}b_{N-j}\Sigma_1^{N-j-1}\Sigma_2^{N-j-1}(\theta_2-\theta_1)^2}{a_{N-j}\theta_1^{\,2}p\Sigma_1^{N-j-1} + b_{N-j}\theta_2^{\,2}p\Sigma_2^{N-j-1}} \simeq qb_{N-j}\Sigma_2^{N-j-1}\frac{(\theta_2-\theta_1)^2}{\theta_1^{\,2}}\left(1 - \frac{b_{N-j}\theta_2^{\,2}q\Sigma_2^{N-j-1}}{a_{N-j}\theta_1^{\,2}p\Sigma_1^{N-j-1}}\right).$$

Hence, for Case 1

$$\rho_{N-j-1} \simeq \left(\frac{1}{\sqrt{2\pi}\sigma}\right)^{N-j-1} \left[(\sigma_{3,N-j-1}^2 + y_{N-j-1}^2)p\Sigma_1^{N-j-1} + \left(\sigma_{4,N-j-1}^2 + y_{N-j-1}^2\left\{1 + \frac{a^2b_{N-j}(\theta_2-\theta_1)^2}{\theta_1^{\,2}}\right\}\right)q\Sigma_2^{N-j-1}\right] + \left(\frac{1}{\sqrt{2\pi}\sigma}\right)^{N-j-1} qb_{N-j}\Sigma_2^{N-j-1}\frac{(\theta_2-\theta)^2}{\theta_1^{\,2}}\frac{b_{N-j}\theta_2^{\,2}q\Sigma_2^{N-j-1}}{a_{N-j}\theta_1^{\,2}p\Sigma_1^{N-j-1}}.$$

Define

$$a_{N-j-1} = 1,$$
$$b_{N-j-1} = 1 + \frac{a^2 b_{N-j}(\theta_2 - \theta_1)^2}{\theta_1^{\,2}}, \tag{H.5}$$

and

$$\epsilon_1 = \left(\frac{1}{\sqrt{2\pi\sigma}}\right)^{N-j-1} q b_{N-j} \Sigma_2^{N-j-1} \frac{(\theta_2 - \theta_1)^2}{\theta_1^{\,2}} \frac{b_{N-j}\theta_2^{\,2} q \Sigma_2^{N-j-1}}{a_{N-j}\theta_1^{\,2} p \Sigma_1^{N-j-1}}.$$

Then,

$$\rho_{N-j-1} \simeq \left(\frac{1}{\sqrt{2\pi\sigma}}\right)^{N-j-1} [(\sigma_{3,N-j-1}^2 + a_{N-j-1} y_{N-j-1}^2) p \Sigma_1^{N-j-1}$$
$$+ (\sigma_{4,N-j-1}^2 + b_{N-j-1} y_{N-j-1}^2 \Sigma_2^{N-j-1}] + \epsilon_1. \tag{H.6}$$

CASE 2. Let us assume that

$$\frac{a_{N-j}\theta_1^{\,2} p \Sigma_1^{N-j-1}}{b_{N-j}\theta_2^{\,2} q \Sigma_2^{N-j-1}} < 1.$$

Since this problem is symmetric in θ_1 and θ_2, the results for this case can be written

$$a_{N-j-1} = 1 + \frac{a^2 a_{N-j}(\theta_2 - \theta_1)^2}{\theta_2^{\,2}},$$
$$b_{N-j-1} = 1, \tag{H.7}$$
$$\epsilon_2 = \left(\frac{1}{\sqrt{2\pi\sigma}}\right)^{N-j-1} p a_{N-j} \Sigma_1^{N-j-1} \frac{(\theta_2 - \theta_1)^2}{\theta_2^{\,2}} \frac{a_{N-j}\theta_1^{\,2} p \Sigma_1^{N-j-1}}{b_{N-j}\theta_2^{\,2} q \Sigma_2^{N-j-1}},$$

and

$$\rho_{N-j-1} \simeq \left(\frac{1}{\sqrt{2\pi\sigma}}\right)^{N-j} [(\sigma_{3,N-j-1}^2 + a_{N-j-1} y_{N-j-1}^2) p \Sigma_1^{N-j-1}$$
$$+ (\sigma_{4,N-j-1}^2 + b_{N-j-1} y_{N-j-1}^2 \Sigma_2^{N-j-1}] + \epsilon_2. \tag{H.8}$$

CASE 3. Finally, consider the case where

$$\frac{a_{N-j}\theta_1^{\,2} p \Sigma_1^{N-j-1}}{b_{N-j}\theta_2^{\,2} q \Sigma_2^{N-j-1}} \simeq 1.$$

Define

$$\Sigma_3^{N-j-1} = a_{N-j}\theta_1^{\,2}p\,\Sigma_1^{N-j-1} - b_{N-j}\theta_2^{\,2}q\,\Sigma_2^{N-j-1}.$$

Then it follows that

$$\frac{pqa_{N-j}b_{N-j}(\theta_2-\theta_1)^2\Sigma_1^{N-j-1}\Sigma_2^{N-j-1}}{a_{N-j}\theta_1^{\,2}p\,\Sigma_1^{N-j-1}+b_{N-j}\theta_2^{\,2}q\,\Sigma_2^{N-j-1}}$$

$$= \frac{pqa_{N-j}b_{N-j}(\theta_2-\theta_1)^2\Sigma_1^{N-j-1}[(a_{N-j}\theta_1^{\,2}p\,\Sigma_1^{N-j-1}-\Sigma_3^{N-j-1})/b_{N-j}\theta_2^{\,2}q]}{2a_{N-j}\theta_1^{\,2}p\,\Sigma_1^{N-j}-\Sigma_3^{N-j}}$$

$$= \frac{pa_{N-j}(\theta_2-\theta_1)^2\Sigma_1^{N-j-1}(1-\Sigma_3^{N-j-1}/a_{N-j}\theta_1^{\,2}p\,\Sigma_1^{N-j-1})}{2\theta_2^{\,2}(1-\Sigma_3^{N-j-1}/2a_{N-j}\theta_1^{\,2}p\,\Sigma_1^{N-j-1})}$$

$$\simeq \frac{pa_{N-j}(\theta_2-\theta_1)^2\Sigma_1^{N-j-1}}{2\theta_2^{\,2}}(1-\Sigma_3^{N-j-1}/a_{N-j}\theta_1^{\,2}p\,\Sigma_1^{N-j-1})$$

$$\times\left[1+\frac{\Sigma_3^{N-j-1}}{2a_{N-j}\theta_1^{\,2}p\,\Sigma_1^{N-j-1}}+(\Sigma_3^{N-j-1}/2a_{N-j}\theta_1^{\,2}p\,\Sigma_1^{N-j-1})^2\right].$$

Expanding the brackets and retaining only second-order terms in Σ_3^{N-j-1},

$$\frac{pqa_{N-j}b_{N-j}(\theta_2-\theta_1)^2\Sigma_1^{N-j-1}\Sigma_2^{N-j-1}}{a_{N-j}\theta_1^{\,2}p\,\Sigma_1^{N-j-1}+b_{N-j}\theta_2^{\,2}q\,\Sigma_2^{N-j-1}}$$

$$\simeq \frac{pa_{N-j}(\theta_2-\theta_1)^2\Sigma_1^{N-j-1}}{2\theta_2^{\,2}}\left[\left(1-\frac{\Sigma_3^{N-j-1}}{2a_{N-j}\theta_1^{\,2}p\,\Sigma_1^{N-j-1}}\right)\right.$$

$$\left.+\left(\frac{\Sigma_3^{N-j-1}}{2a_{N-j}\theta_1^{\,2}p\,\Sigma_1^{N-j-1}}\right)^2-\frac{1}{2}\left(\frac{\Sigma_3^{N-j-1}}{a_{N-j}\theta_1^{\,2}p\,\Sigma_1^{N-j-1}}\right)^2\right]$$

$$\simeq \frac{pa_{N-j}(\theta_2-\theta_1)^2\Sigma_1^{N-j-1}}{2\theta_2^{\,2}} - \Sigma_3^{N-j-1}\frac{(\theta_2-\theta_1)^2}{4\theta_2^{\,2}\theta_1^{\,2}}$$

$$-\frac{1}{4}\left(\frac{\Sigma_3^{N-j-1}}{a_{N-j}\theta_1^{\,2}p\,\Sigma_1^{N-j-1}}\right)^2\frac{pa_{N-j}(\theta_2-\theta_1)^2\Sigma_1^{N-j-1}}{2\theta_2^{\,2}}$$

$$\simeq \frac{(\theta_2 - \theta_1)^2}{4\theta_2^{\,2}} a_{N-j} p \Sigma_1^{N-j-1} + \frac{(\theta_2 - \theta_1)^2}{4\theta_1^{\,2}} b_{N-j} q \Sigma_2^{N-j-1}$$

$$- \frac{1}{4}\left(1 - \frac{b_{N-j}\theta_2^{\,2} q \Sigma_2^{N-j-1}}{a_{N-j}\theta_1^{\,2} p \Sigma_1^{N-j-1}}\right)^2 \frac{p a_{N-j}(\theta_2 - \theta_1)^2 \Sigma_1^{N-j-1}}{2\theta_2^{\,2}} .$$

Let us define the following parameters:

$$a_{N-j-1} = 1 + a^2 \frac{(\theta_2 - \theta_2)^2}{4\theta_2^{\,2}} a_{N-j} ,$$

$$b_{N-j-1} = 1 + a^2 \frac{(\theta_2 - \theta_1)^2}{4\theta_1^{\,2}} b_{N-j} , \qquad \text{(H.9)}$$

and

$$\epsilon_3 = \frac{1}{4}\left(\frac{1}{\sqrt{2\pi\sigma}}\right)^{N-j-1} \left(1 - \frac{b_{N-j}\theta_2^{\,2} q \Sigma_2^{N-j-1}}{a_{N-j}\theta_1^{\,2} p \Sigma_1^{N-j-1}}\right)^2 \frac{p a_{N-j}(\theta_2 - \theta_1)^2 \Sigma_1^{N-j-1}}{2\theta_2^{\,2}} .$$

Then we have

$$\rho_{N-j-1} \cong \left(\frac{1}{\sqrt{2\pi\sigma}}\right)^{N-j-1} [(\sigma_{3,N-j-1}^2 + a_{N-j-1} y_{N-j-1}^2) p \Sigma_1^{N-j-1}$$

$$+ (\sigma_{4,N-j-1}^2 + b_{N-j-1} y_{N-j-1}^2) q \Sigma_2^{N-j-1}] + \epsilon_3 . \qquad \text{(H.10)}$$

Author Index

Numbers in italics refer to pages on which the complete references are listed.

Subject Index